INTENTIONAL PARENTING

PARENTING

— 10 WAYS TO BE AN —

EXCEPTIONAL PARENT

IN A **QUICK FIX** WORLD

DOUG & CATHY FIELDS

Intentional Parenting: 10 Ways to Be an Exceptional Parent in a Quick-Fix World

Published by Orange, a division of The reThink Group, Inc.
5870 Charlotte Lane, Suite 300 Cumming, GA 30040 U.S.A.
The Orange logo is a registered trademark of The reThink Group, Inc.

ISBN-13: 978-1-63570-086-2

Special thanks to Peter R. Marsh and Kitchen Table Academy for their support and leadership in the production of this Workbook.

Time over time concept and marbles illustration on page 20 used by permission of The Phase Project, Reggie Joiner, Kristen Ivy and Orange/reThink.
For more information, access www.PhaseGuides.com.

Project Producer: Andrew Accardy for Kitchen Table Academy
Kitchen Table Academy would like to thank Melissa Accardy, Linda Dean, Mark MacDonald, Brian Bird, Bill Daily, B.J. Marsh, Byron Van Kley, Jim Burns, Seth Bartlette, Matt Pope and Fadi & Kim Cheikha for their support and valuable contributions.
Special thanks to Peter R. Marsh for his concern for parents and his wisdom in guiding this project.

Art Design: Ashley Swanson & Seth Bartlette

Printed in the United States of America
First Edition
4 5 6 7 8 9 10 11 12 13

TABLE OF CONTENTS

START HERE

WELCOME TO THE CRAZY, FAST-MOVING, PARENTING JOURNEY

START HERE: **WELCOME TO THE CRAZY, FAST-MOVING, PARENTING JOURNEY**

Intentional Parenting is an interactive series made up of three components. As you follow the prompts in the workbook you will:

> ▶ **1) WATCH THE TEACHING VIDEO WITH DOUG**
>
> 👤 **2) COMPLETE THE WORKBOOK ACTIVITIES**
>
> ▶ **3) WATCH THE DISCUSSION WITH DOUG & CATHY**

Each short video will cover two actions at a time while the workbook will address one action per chapter, so you will watch the video and then complete two chapters in the workbook.

1) STRONG BELIEF
2) 24/7 ROLE MODEL

3) ENCOURAGING WORDS
4) GENUINE AFFECTION

7) DELICATE DISCIPLINE
8) ACTIVATE RESPONSIBILITY

5) CONSISTENT PRESENCE
6) PEACEFUL HOME

9) POSITIVE MEMORIES
10) SERIOUS FUN

◈ A NOTE FROM DOUG & CATHY

When we were kids, we never gave thought to the fact that our moms and dads didn't have a clue as to what they were actually doing when it came to parenting. We naively assumed they were expert parents. Our view became enlightened when we became parents 27 years ago and soon realized, "Wait! Our parents have been faking it! They didn't know what they were doing! They've been making everything up along the way." As children we viewed them as "experts" because they were great at hiding their fear and uncertainty. But, now as adults, we knew better and we had to begin our own journey to figure out how to be good parents.

Our assumption is that you're reading this workbook because that's what you want too. You want to be good parents and lovingly guide your children to a place of health and independence where they leave your home not being "totally screwed up." If that's you… we're excited to help you on your journey.

Let's begin with some truth-telling: Parenting is difficult!

Single parents might argue that the word "difficult" should be replaced with "impossible." If you are a single parent, you fall into our "hero" category. We're in constant amazement at how single parents are able to do everything they do.

Yes it's hard. But what you do as a parent every day and every week matters. Your actions — over time — are the single greatest influence in the life of your child.

Because of this truth, our primary goal for this workbook and videos is to provide you with 10 specific actions you can take that will help you become a more effective parent.

That's why we've called this Intentional Parenting. Good parents are intentional parents. It's the opposite of…

Reactive Parenting,
Spontaneous Parenting,
Fly-by-the-seat-of-your-pants Parenting.

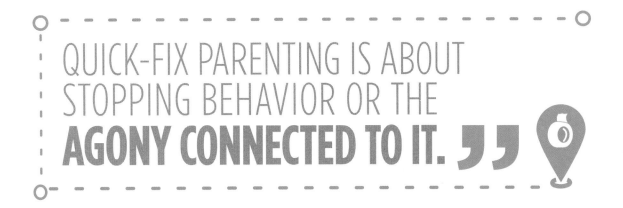

◈ QUICK-FIX PARENTING

Very few parents enter into the parenting responsibility with a high degree of confidence feeling fully prepared. Most of us joined the parenting ranks with good intentions and excitement. But, since our children didn't arrive wrapped in a how-to instruction manual, most of us wind up relying on something we refer to as Quick-Fix Parenting. At its foundation, Quick-Fix Parenting becomes about stopping the behavior *or* the agony connected to it — which is often the parent's pain.

Quick-Fix Parenting is exactly like what it sounds — a quick fix to a problem. It's not necessarily a good fix or a healthy fix or an empowering fix, and it's definitely not an effective long-term strategy. Most parents embrace Quick-Fix Parenting because…

- it was modeled by their parents and that's all they know,
- it's easier, more convenient, and relies on impulse rather than intellect,
- it can be effective in stopping and correcting a child's behavior in the moment to quench potential conflict.

If this describes you… that's okay for now. Most parents start here, but we don't want you to stay here. Instead, we want to show you a better way to navigate through the parenting land mines we all face with an intentional approach to parenting.

◉ OVER TIME

We are veteran parents… not perfect parents. Definitely not perfect! (Ask our kids.) While raising our kids we blinked somewhere along the way and now all our kids are in their 20's. Time moved on… and it moved rapidly. Time didn't wait for us to get our parenting act together. Time won't wait for you either.

Time is one of the consistent realities of life—regardless of language, culture, region, intellect, religion, and economics. All humans share this in common: sixty seconds to a minute, sixty minutes to an hour, twenty-four hours to a day, and 365 days to a year. Time clicks on. Time matters.

TIME MATTERS.

Your child's 18th birthday makes up 6,570 days. That calculates to 936 weeks or only 216 months.

The brevity of those 216 months requires you to develop some intentional parenting actions so you don't miss out on your opportunity. Scripture teaches us of this same principle:

Teach us to number our days, that we may gain a heart of wisdom. Psalm 90:12 (NIV)

We believe that one of your best parenting moves to maximize this movement of time is to commit to the 10 intentional actions that are discussed throughout this workbook and video series.

We didn't do everything right as parents, and we've got our share of regrets, but we fought against Quick-Fix Parenting in order to become Intentional Parents. We did this in front of an audience.

We were both ministry leaders and speakers in one of the largest churches in the country and were on display in front of thousands of families every week. Throughout those years we've had parents literally beg us to share our parenting principles. This might come across as odd, but this workbook is really the result of several couples wearing us down with the hope that they could "capture our secrets." While we can't guarantee you'll have our same results, we do believe that what we present here are some Biblical, relational, and intentional actions that will enhance your odds — over time.

One last note before you begin, and please read this carefully: as intentional as you plan to be, and as active as you are in implementing what we suggest, we have to admit that there is an element of mystery that surrounds the parent/child relationship. All children are different and come with their own unique brand of free will. There is no one set of parenting principles that works for every child. We've seen amazing kids emerge from lousy parents — and the opposite is true too — amazing parents can have kids who struggle. But what we can tell you is that if you apply these principles the odds of your children growing up to be healthy, independent, young adults will increase dramatically.

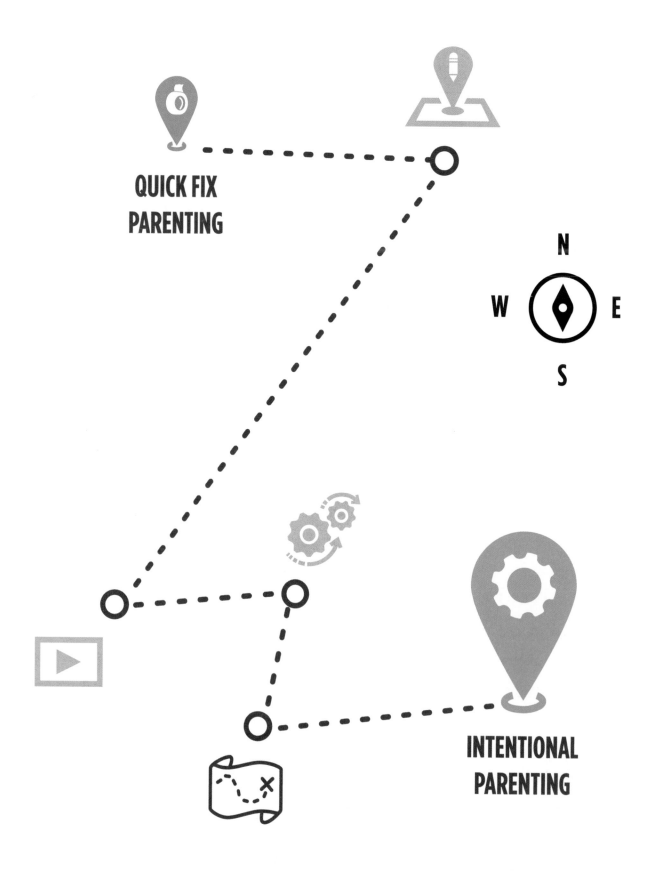

QUICK FIX
PARENTING

INTENTIONAL
PARENTING

MAP LEGEND

NAVIGATING THE INTENTIONAL PARENTING WORKBOOK

We're excited that you're about to embark on a journey through the Intentional Parenting workbook and we want to guide you along the way. Throughout, you will see various colorful icons. This is our way of pointing out a particular action step, a phrase to remember, or important thought to consider. Take a look at this map legend to learn more about the map markers.

INTENTIONAL PARENTING

LEAN-IN, WRITE THIS DOWN, AND LEARN MORE. THIS WILL POINT YOU IN THE RIGHT DIRECTION AND WILL GUIDE YOU BEYOND THOSE QUICK-FIX SHORTCUTS.

VIDEO REMINDER

TIME TO PUT THE PENCILS DOWN AND LEARN FROM THE INTENTIONAL PARENTING VIDEOS. THIS WILL LET YOU KNOW WHICH VIDEO SESSION TO WATCH ALONG THE WAY.

QUICK-FIX PARENTING

WATCH OUT! CAUTION! TURN AROUND! THESE REPRESENT NEGATIVE AREAS IN OUR PARENTING TO AVOID AT ALL COSTS.

NAVIGATION

DON'T GET LOST! THIS ICON WILL POINT OUT ALL OF THE STEPS YOU WILL TAKE IN YOUR JOURNEY. FOLLOW THESE ALONG AND YOU'LL BE SURE TO FIND YOUR WAY.

JOURNEY TIPS

TAKE NOTE! LET US HELP YOU ON YOUR JOURNEY BY POINTING OUT SOME PRACTICAL AND HELPFUL INSIGHTS FOR YOU TO CONSIDER.

TAKE ACTION

DON'T MISS THIS IMPORTANT STEP! EACH CHAPTER IN THIS WORKBOOK ENDS WITH A CALL TO ACTION. THIS WILL HELP YOU PERSONALIZE THE JOURNEY.

ACTIVITIES

GRAB THOSE PENCILS AND TAKE ACTION! THIS WILL NOTIFY YOU OF A BRIEF AND ENGAGING ACTIVITY. TAKE TIME TO PAUSE AND COMPLETE THESE BEFORE PROCEEDING.

ACTION 1
STRONG BELIEF

ACTION 1 **STRONG BELIEF**

Intentional Parents believe they have incredible influence on their children.

Watch the "Strong Belief & 24/7 Role Model" Teaching Video prior to reading this chapter.

Brace yourself: you're about to begin a journey that could change the way you parent and redirect the course of your child's life. Are you thinking, "Wow, That's a bold statement!"? We know it is, but we don't say it out of arrogance. Rather, we have confidence that comes from our own parenting journey that has been filled with failures and setbacks, but also victories and a lot of fun. Based on our personal experiences and our work with thousands of families, we have strong convictions about these parenting principles we're going to share with you. We believe they will help you, and, just as importantly, we believe they're doable.

The first essential action in becoming an Intentional Parent is strong belief. You must believe that you are the most significant influence in the life of your child. Parents who don't believe this truth minimize the incredible responsibility God has given them.

In our parenting seminars we are often asked questions that reveal parents' fears about the negative influence of media, culture, and peers on their children. This is a normal concern in today's crazy culture, but we answer their worry by telling them to be less concerned about "outside" influences and more concerned about their hugely significant roles as the primary influencers in their child's lives.

Believe it or not, more than anyone else, kids of all ages are influenced and shaped by their parents' actions, beliefs, and values. This influence only shifts away from parents to other influences when the parents are either physically or emotionally absent. If moms and dads step out of the parenting scene, culture and all it represents is willing and glad to step in.

YOUR ROLE MATTERS

Your influence is why you are such a big deal as a parent! This should be no surprise since children are very valuable to God.

Look how Jesus describes children:

> *He [Jesus] took a little child and had him stand among them. Taking him in his arms, he said to them, "Whoever welcomes one of these little children in my name welcomes me; and whoever welcomes me does not welcome me but the one who sent me." Mark 9:36-37 (NIV)*

When you welcome a child into your life, you welcome Jesus. That's powerful! Children are valued by God. You were called to be a parent — it's a significant part of your destiny and life purpose. Becoming an Intentional Parent will be one of the most important actions you ever take.

Here's what the writer of Psalms says:

> *"Children are a gift from the LORD; they are a reward from him..." Psalms 127:3 (NLT)*

God has rewarded you with the gift of a child — a gift worthy of cherishing and one that requires your very best effort.

Your first step is to simply believe you are vital to the health and development of your child. Your parenting matters — your child's future is on the line.

ACTIVITY:
YOUR ROLE MATTERS

Let's pause and consider how your parenting might be different if you really believed you were the most significant person in the life of your child. Next to the phrases below, circle the number that best describes your current belief.

NOT BUYING IT			HAVE SERIOUS DOUBTS			COULD BELIEVE IT		STRONGLY BELIEVE	

Without a doubt, I'm the strongest influence in my child's life.

| 1 | 2 | 3 | 4 | 5 | 6 | 7 | 8 | 9 | 10 |

My child is a gift from God especially for me.

| 1 | 2 | 3 | 4 | 5 | 6 | 7 | 8 | 9 | 10 |

One of the most spiritual actions I can take is to be intentional in my parenting.

| 1 | 2 | 3 | 4 | 5 | 6 | 7 | 8 | 9 | 10 |

My parenting efforts are worth my very best energy.

| 1 | 2 | 3 | 4 | 5 | 6 | 7 | 8 | 9 | 10 |

Even if I have struggled as a parent, I can still have significant influence on my child.

| 1 | 2 | 3 | 4 | 5 | 6 | 7 | 8 | 9 | 10 |

Which of the statements above is the most difficult for you to believe? Why do you think that is?

_____

_____

Is there anything keeping you from believing that you are the most significant person in your child's life? If so, what?

_____

_____

Does Strong Belief feel more like a burden, or does it feel more hopeful? Explain.

_____

_____

PARENTING AS A PRIORITY

Most parents have a basic understanding that their parenting roles are important, albeit many are insecure about how to be good parents. Strong Belief is the foundation for everything else in this series, and our hope is that you'll release any guilt you may have about the past. We want to challenge you to develop a deep conviction that your role is crucial, and over time your intentional actions will reap powerful rewards.

You must strongly believe that you are the most influential person in your child's life and take responsibility for it. This belief combined with the specific actions from this series will change the way you parent. Belief is big… but turning belief into action is even bigger.

The ten actions we're going to look at in this series will require you to prioritize your lifestyle and schedule to reflect Strong Belief in your parenting role. Intentional Parents are clear about these priorities, and in this order:

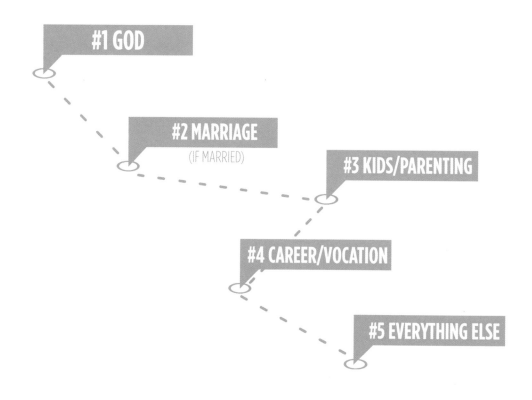

#1 GOD

#2 MARRIAGE
(IF MARRIED)

#3 KIDS/PARENTING

#4 CAREER/VOCATION

#5 EVERYTHING ELSE

ACTIVITY:
PARENTING AS PRIORITY

Do you agree with the order of these priorities? If not, what do you think should be different?

_____

_____

_____

How would you currently evaluate your life in these specific areas? Think about what gets most of your time and attention, and then rank the following numerically.

_____ A personal, growing relationship with God

_____ Marriage (if married)

_____ Kids/Parenting

_____ Career/Vocation

_____ Friends

_____ Sports/Hobbies

_____ Church Involvement/Activities

_____ Other: (describe) _____

Are you happy with where you ranked parenting in the list above? If not, what changes may you need to make in order to reprioritize?

_____

_____

_____

_____

_____

_____

_____

_____

_____

_____

◈ EXPERTS SPEAK

Research and social science studies support the fact that the parent/child relationship significantly impacts a child throughout his or her lifetime. The parent's role and involvement is essential to the child's development of emotional health, academic advancement, and making significant life decisions.

"… parenting goes far beyond the requirements for meeting the basic survival needs of the child, and parents have a significant influence on how children turn out, including their personality, emotional development, and behavioral habits, as well as a host of other factors. It is important for the overall development of children that parents be present enough to support them, and this support fosters confidence and growth in many areas." [1]

"… a lack of parental involvement can have long-lasting negative effects on a child. Children who don't have a close relationship with a parent are at risk for teen pregnancy, more likely to drink alcohol or smoke cigarettes, and more likely to live a sedentary life. They are also more likely to be withdrawn or suffer from depression." [2]

"...the parent/child relationship significantly impacts a child throughout his/her lifetime."

1. Alexandra Murphy, Parental Influence on the Emotional Development of Children

https://my.vanderbilt.edu/developmentalpsychologyblog/2014/05/parental-influence-on-the-emotional-development-of-children/

2. Alice Drinkworth, Positive & Negative Influences of Parents on Their Children

http://everydaylife.globalpost.com/positive-negative-influences-parents-children-6070.html

ACTIVITY:
EXPERTS SPEAK

What, if anything, from these two quotes was empowering to you? Why?

_____

_____

_____

Did anything strike you as unsettling? Why?

_____

_____

_____

Think of your own childhood and the example that was set for you. How involved and intentional were your parents?

_____

_____

_____

What are some positive actions you learned from your parents?

_____

_____

_____

What negative actions do you want to do differently than your parents?

_____

_____

_____

BEGINNING WITH THE END IN MIND

One way to strengthen your belief is by starting with the end in mind. Your child's 18th birthday marks the first 6,570 days of his life … which is 936 weeks … or 216 months.

We have a good friend who presents new parents with a decorative jar containing 936 marbles. Every week parents are to remove a marble in order to be reminded of how quickly the gift of time disappears. Since parents are going to "lose their marbles" anyway, this visual aid serves as a prompt for them to be intentional with their remaining time.

 LOSING YOUR MARBLES

| BIRTH | PRE-K | 2ND GRADE | 6TH GRADE | FRESHMAN | SENIOR | GRADUATION |

Let's do a little math. List your kids' names below and write out how many months, weeks, and days (at least approximate) are left before each child turns 18.

Name:	Months	Weeks	Days
_____	_____	_____	_____
_____	_____	_____	_____
_____	_____	_____	_____
_____	_____	_____	_____

SEE THE WEEKS YOU HAVE LEFT AT **THEPARENTCUE.ORG/APP**

ACTIVITY:
BEGINNING WITH THE END IN MIND

When you look at the time remaining until your children turn 18, how do you feel?

_____

_____

What specific fears do you have?

_____

_____

No caring parents are just biding their time until their children leave home. All of us have dreams for our kids. We passionately want them to become a certain type of person — one that's prepared and well equipped to succeed in life. Take a few minutes to think about what kind of qualities you want your kids to possess when they graduate high school and prepare to live on their own. Write down as many ideas as come to mind.

[Note: Keep in mind, we're not pushing for specific right or wrong answers here; instead, we're asking you to dream with an end in mind. Wisdom would teach us that he or she who aims at nothing will reach it every time.]

_____	_____
_____	_____
_____	_____
_____	_____
_____	_____
_____	_____

When you have the end in mind, not only can you be more intentional about how to guide your children, but your belief and resolve will also be strengthened along the way as you focus in and fight for that big picture.

Here is an example of five end-in-mind targets we defined that have helped aim us in the right direction. We wanted our children...

1. To Display Confidence: we observed so many insecure children who lacked basic self-assurance. Without confidence, kids often become victims or followers of others.

2. To Express Character: we wanted our children to develop a moral foundation and have a solid understanding of what is right and wrong. Character influences decision making.

3. To Have Strong Convictions: character without a set of beliefs or convictions is empty. Our dream was for our kids' convictions to be based on the teachings of God's Word. We wanted to introduce them to the person and power of Jesus and pray that their faith would become their own.

4. To Show Compassion: this is closely connected to character and convictions, but we chose to give it its own theme. We wanted to make sure our kids understood that our world is filled with pain and suffering everywhere, and the Jesus they follow requires them to care.

5. To Become Competent: ultimately, at the end of their time with us, we wanted our children to possess certain skills that would serve them well (i.e. people-skills, work-ethic, ability to navigate finances, relational/emotional intelligence, and so on.)

ACTIVITY:
BEGINNING WITH THE END IN MIND

Now you try. Look at your list on page 21 and try to bundle them into themes of your own. Notice our five qualities are based on inner values and not outer performance (i.e. grades, athletics, popularity, etc.). We're not suggesting you copy our five themes; rather use them as an example to help deepen your thinking about your own end game.

_____

_____

_____

_____

_____

If it's helpful, use this chart below.

OUR THEMES:	YOUR THEMES:
CONFIDENCE	
CHARACTER	
CONVICTIONS	
COMPASSION	
COMPETENCE	

Final step. Take some time to turn your themes into phrases that you'll remember, i.e. To Display Confidence, To Express Character, etc.)

Write your final list here:

_____

_____

_____

_____

_____

_____

_____

_____

_____

_____

_____

_____

_____

_____

_____

Great job! Now you have some goals and a more defined and clear destination. We encourage you to seek out feedback about what you listed from parents, grandparents, and friends. Consider this a "work in progress," and continue to reflect on and refine your list until you sense a firm conviction.

TAKE ACTION

What is one action you might take this week to strengthen your belief as a parent?

_____

_____

Is there anything that needs to change in order for you to commit to being an Intentional Parent? If so, what?

_____

_____

Write out a short purpose statement to become a guide to your parenting. It does not have to be a final draft, just list a few words you can easily remember (i.e "No quick fixes," "Every day matters," "Keep the end in mind.")

_____

_____

_____

You are on the path to becoming an Intentional Parent. It won't always be easy, but if you keep the end in mind and ask God to guide you along the way, you are on your way to having a huge, positive impact on the life of your child. Believe it!

Please watch the "Strong Belief & 24/7 Role Model" Discussion Video with Doug & Cathy.

ACTION 2
24/7 ROLE MODEL

Intentional Parents understand that children learn from observing them as their primary role models.

If you have not already done so, watch the "Strong Belief & 24/7 Role Model" Teaching Video prior to reading this chapter.

When our son was little he would always interrupt us by saying, "Mom, Dad, watch me!" Then he would do something that he thought was entertaining. It sometimes was as simple as jumping off one stair. Honestly, it was usually something silly that didn't require much fine motor skill. He just wanted us to watch him, and his default "get our attention line" was: "Mom, Dad, watch me!"

As he grew up we began to notice that his desire for us to watch him became less, yet he began to more closely watch us. He never said it aloud, but we knew he had transitioned from "Mom, Dad, watch me!" to now thinking, "I'm watching you, Mom and Dad."

There's no question that parents serve as significant role models to their children. The real question is: what kind of role model are you?

In the Strong Belief section we asked you to think of the parental influence you have on your child. This second action of an Intentional Parent now forces you to consider what you're teaching your children through how you live your life.

You can't escape it — your children are stealing parts of your character, and they are going to end up looking like you. You've heard it said…

"She's a chip off the old block."
"He's the flip side of the same coin."
"The apple doesn't fall far from the tree."
"Like father, like son. Like mother, like daughter."
"She sure lives up to the family name."

Your life is on display, and your children are always watching and learning from you — both good and bad characteristics and behaviors. Intentional Parents understand this reality and consider the messages their actions are sending. They become more thoughtful about their own lifestyles and what they're passing on to their kids.

Your children are watching and learning from you…

- How you think
- How you treat others
- How you pray
- How you talk about those who are hurting
- What you do with your finances
- How you make decisions
- How you respond to pain
- What, why, and how often you eat
- What you watch on TV
- How consumed you are with social media
- How you prioritize
- How you drive a car
- When you're happy… when you're sad
- How you talk about those who are less fortunate
- How you reconcile conflict
- Where you place the value of faith conversations

An Intentional Parent takes the time to seriously consider these and many other messages. A Quick-Fix Parent simply relies on the phrase, "Don't do as I do, do as I say," when it comes to their lifestyle. This is as weak as it is hypocritical.

Not only is the clock of time always running (remember your child's 18th birthday makes up 6,570 days, is 936 weeks, or only 216 months)... but so is the surveillance camera that's pointed at your life — it's "ON" 24/7. Every day you are teaching your children something about how they are to live their lives.

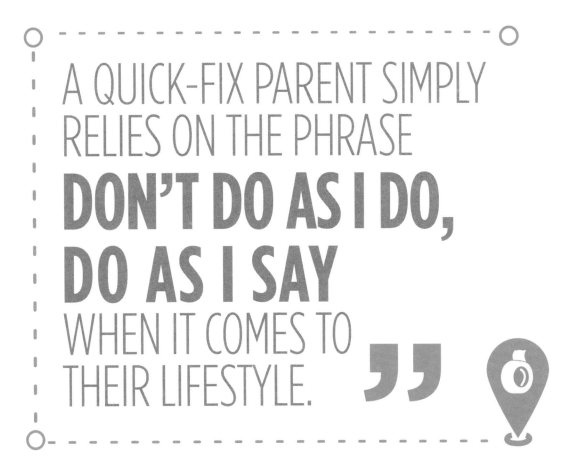

A QUICK-FIX PARENT SIMPLY RELIES ON THE PHRASE **DON'T DO AS I DO, DO AS I SAY** WHEN IT COMES TO THEIR LIFESTYLE. "

ACTIVITY:
ROLE MODEL

Let's think deeply for a minute: is the dream you created for your children (on page 21) being reinforced by how you are currently living your life?

Check the box that best applies to your current overall situation:

☐ My life is mostly consistent with how I want my kids to live.
☐ My life sends mixed messages to my kids about what I expect from them.
☐ If I really am being watched closely...my kids are in trouble.

Let's make this more specific: circle the number that best represents these different areas of your life:

DON'T WATCH THIS AREA OF MY LIFE				I'M FAIRLY CONSISTENT			WATCH ME!		

My faith

| 1 | 2 | 3 | 4 | 5 | 6 | 7 | 8 | 9 | 10 |

How I/we handle our finances

| 1 | 2 | 3 | 4 | 5 | 6 | 7 | 8 | 9 | 10 |

My marriage/my singleness

| 1 | 2 | 3 | 4 | 5 | 6 | 7 | 8 | 9 | 10 |

My friendships

| 1 | 2 | 3 | 4 | 5 | 6 | 7 | 8 | 9 | 10 |

My integrity/honesty

| 1 | 2 | 3 | 4 | 5 | 6 | 7 | 8 | 9 | 10 |

My ability to deal with anger

| 1 | 2 | 3 | 4 | 5 | 6 | 7 | 8 | 9 | 10 |

Language: critical, negative, cursing

| 1 | 2 | 3 | 4 | 5 | 6 | 7 | 8 | 9 | 10 |

Language: positive, encouraging, kind

| 1 | 2 | 3 | 4 | 5 | 6 | 7 | 8 | 9 | 10 |

My displays of affection

| 1 | 2 | 3 | 4 | 5 | 6 | 7 | 8 | 9 | 10 |

My ability to have fun and laugh

| 1 | 2 | 3 | 4 | 5 | 6 | 7 | 8 | 9 | 10 |

My compassion for those hurting or less fortunate

| 1 | 2 | 3 | 4 | 5 | 6 | 7 | 8 | 9 | 10 |

How I manage my time and priorities

| 1 | 2 | 3 | 4 | 5 | 6 | 7 | 8 | 9 | 10 |

My availability to my family

| 1 | 2 | 3 | 4 | 5 | 6 | 7 | 8 | 9 | 10 |

How I manage conflict

| 1 | 2 | 3 | 4 | 5 | 6 | 7 | 8 | 9 | 10 |

Put an asterisk (*) by the three that received the lowest rankings. Begin praying about and thinking more deeply about the example you're setting for your kids.

When we talk to parents about role modeling, the stereotypical first response is defensiveness. This is understandable. It can be a jarring reality if you've never taken time t seriously consider that your children are taking notes on your life.

Please don't become discouraged, though. All parents make mistakes! There is no such thing as a perfect parent — there never has been and there never will be. Intentional Parents know they will make mistakes, but they're also willing to hold up the mirror and learn how their choices and actions contribute to their kids' choices and actions.

HOLDING UP THE MIRROR

We have some friends who wanted to talk to us about their sixth grade son who wa cheating at school. They were quite embarrassed to get a call from his teacher, and then a couple weeks later another call from the principle informing them of a repeat offense When they told us their story, they made statements like, "I don't know where he picked this up," and "Everyone cheats at school occasionally, but he's the one who got caught."

I (Cathy) am not sure what got into me in the moment, but I took a big gulp and said, "Is there any chance he has ever seen either of you cheat?" This comment was followed by nervous laughter as the husband jokingly said, "He doesn't even know anything about our taxes."

Here's why I made the bold comment: studies reveal that kids are cheating more and more. Why is that? Is it because education is more difficult? Hardly. One reason is because kids have been tutored, during their growing years, on how to lie and cheat at home.

Consider the "little ways" children experience "truth being stretched."

They listen to parents' phone conversations and hear exaggerations and fabrications.

A parent might say, "Don't tell them your real age — we'll save money paying a child's admission instead of an adult price."

What about when one parent says, "Don't tell your mom/dad about this; I don't want her/him to get mad at me."

Children hear many of these "little fibs" that add up to one big integrity problem. As an Intentional Parent, when you blow it… and you will… simply apologize. When you do, you are intentionally modeling an act you want your child to adopt. Over time, this act will be caught and he or she will actually come to respect you more.

We are fully aware of how difficult it is to admit when you're wrong. The quick-fix approach is to sweep your dishonesty under the rug and move on pretending it wasn't seen, heard, caught, or experienced. That's not the route of integrity, though.

Here's some suggested language you might consider learning and using with your children:

"I know you heard me lie to Mr. Gutridge. Truthfully, I was just too tired and didn't want to spend time helping him. Please forgive me. I'm going over there now, and I'm going to give him a hand and apologize to him too."

"I want to apologize to you for not telling mom the entire truth. You heard us talking and I know I didn't tell her exactly what happened about why you and I were late coming home last night. I was trying to keep her from getting angry and I lied. I've already asked for her forgiveness and I want to ask for yours too."

"I'm sorry about asking you not to tell Mom that I bought you candy. That was wrong to put you in that position, and it was dishonest for me to withhold the truth. I need forgiveness from both of you."

Of course your kids already know you're not perfect, but what they may not know is what they're supposed to do when they mess up. They need you to model it. We've had to apologize to our kids more times than we want to admit, but as they matured we began to hear our own vocabulary repeated back to us.

> **YOUR KIDS ALREADY KNOW YOU'RE NOT PERFECT,** BUT WHAT THEY MAY NOT KNOW IS WHAT THEY'RE SUPPOSED TO DO WHEN THEY MESS UP. **THEY NEED YOU TO MODEL IT.**

ACTIVITY:
HOLDING UP THE MIRROR

When you've blown it, and your kids have a front row seat to observe your mistake(s), what is your normal response?

_____

_____

Do you ever ask your child to forgive you when you've made a mistake? Why or why not?

_____

_____

Consider this comment: *"I didn't make the right choice when I lied to your school about you being sick. I took the easy but wrong route, because I didn't want the hassle of explaining myself."*

Why is this type of confession (from parent to child) so difficult?

_____

_____

What message do you think confession sends to your children?

_____

_____

What's a recent situation where you've found yourself "caught" by your kid(s)?

_____

_____

ACTIVITY:
HOLDING UP THE MIRROR (CONT'D)

How did you handle it? How do you think they felt about you afterward?

_____

_____

How do you typically feel about your child when you catch him/her in a lie? Disrespected? Sad? Embarrassed? How do you think your kids feel when they catch you "stretching the truth"?

_____

_____

In King David's prayer of praise he says, _"I know, my God, that you test the heart and are pleased with integrity." 1 Chronicles 29:17a (NIV)_

If your heart was being tested today, how would you score on integrity?

| 1 | 2 | 3 | 4 | 5 | 6 | 7 | 8 | 9 | 10 |

Did you find it difficult to circle a number? If so, that might be a warning sign for you to consider.

THE BATON OF FAITH

Let's consider another value that is being modeled to your children: your faith.

The following scripture is very clear that we are to pass on the baton of faith to our children.

> *"Love the Lord your God with all your heart and with all your soul and with all your strength. These commandments that I give you today are to be on your heart. Impress them on your children. Talk about them when you sit at home or when you walk along the road, when you lie down or when you get up. Tie them as symbols on your hands and bind them on your foreheads." Deuteronomy 6:5-8 (NIV)*

If you look closely at this Scripture you'll see the parent is tasked with taking action to both embrace the commands of God (they are to be on your heart) and to pass them on to the child (impress them on your children, talk about them). This isn't to be done through a one-time conversation, rather it's to happen on a regular basis (at home, while out walking, when going to bed, and when waking up).

Our experience has been that the faith conversations we had with our children had to be validated by our lifestyle. We could tell them that Jesus makes a difference in one's life, but as they grew up they needed to see it in our lives. They had to experience first-hand that mom and dad had a genuine faith that was more than "talk."

This is so important to understand: your kids don't need you to be a perfect parent or a spiritual giant. The perception of perfection and overly spiritual parents can produce intimidation and create insecurity. We've come to believe that our kids most needed to see a mom and dad who weren't just wearing the label "Christian," but were genuinely trying to follow the person and teachings of Jesus. We didn't do it perfectly (and you won't either), but they knew our faith was important and central to who we are and how we think and live.

ACTIVITY:
THE BATON OF FAITH

Re-read those few verses on page 37 and either circle or underline key words or phrases. Why did they strike you as significant?

_____

_____

What do you think it means for you to "impress them on your children"?

_____

_____

This Scripture places high priority on the frequency of talking to our children about the commands of God. Think about how you might do this with your own parenting.

- At home?
- When you're out walking around?
- When you're lying down?
- When you're getting up?

What are other contemporary places that might be conducive for faith conversations? (For example, a car ride, at a sporting event, etc.)

_____

_____

Put a check mark by the statement below that most clearly applies to you. If you're married, put "SP" in front of the one you think best describes your spouse.

- ☐ *My faith is very important to me.*
- ☐ *My faith is pretty important, but not most important.*
- ☐ *Some days my faith is important, some days it isn't.*
- ☐ *If I'm really honest, I don't think that much about my faith.*
- ☐ *I'm not a person of faith.*
- ☐ *I'm anti-faith.*

ACTIVITY:
THE BATON OF FAITH (CONT'D)

When it comes to you following the person and teachings of Jesus, what is the consistent message your children are seeing?

_____

_____

_____

_____

Are you and your spouse in agreement about faith values? If not, you should probably spend some time talking about both of your desires and expectations related to faith. Ideally, what is the primary message you want your children to see regarding your faith?

_____

_____

_____

_____

What may need to change about your decisions and priorities for them to see what you want them to see?

_____

_____

_____

_____

_____

_____

_____

Over the years parents have asked us about our own faith conversations, which they usually label "family devotions." Cathy and I look at each other, smile, and think, "Now they'll know the truth." The truth is that we weren't very successful at a formal time of family devotions. Once our kids were old enough to get up and walk away, or realize that body noises or giggles could quench the Spirit... well, we sort of gave up on the "sit down so we can give you an insightful lecture of God's Word" approach. Instead, we chose a different type of strategy and learned to point to Jesus in our normal conversations daily. We aren't the types to over-spiritualize everything, but as Deuteronomy 6 states, we had constant conversations. Our goal was to help our kids recognize that Jesus is here now and not a distant deity, and that His love for us is our motivation to take the right actions. These types of intentional faith conversations became our "family devotions."

OTHERS AS THE ROLE MODEL

If you study emotionally healthy kids, you'll discover that regardless of where they come from — Cambodian refugee camps, inner city housing projects, or upper class, suburban families — healthy kids have role models in their lives. In addition to their parents, there are others who walk with them and love on them during their growing-up years.

This truth is one of the many reasons the church body is so beautiful: it's an army of people who have put their faith in Jesus and express that faith by loving others. These lives impact other lives. Your children don't have to grow up without a large community of believers. The church is family, and families care for the people in their family. The church can become a place where people invest their time into your kids, coming alongside them and helping them grow.

If you're not part of a faith-community, or you can't find these people at your church, you must keep looking for other significant adults to come alongside your kids. Even great parents are in need of others to invest in their children. Our own three children are a product of Intentional Parents AND Significant Others who have guided, mentored, and loved them throughout their elementary, junior high, high school, and young adult years. We are always quick to point out the influence of others on our children's emotional and spiritual health.

Here's the good news: you have some really great qualities that your kids are picking up from you. Sometimes we tend to focus on our negative characteristics and forget about the positive things we're passing on. Let's be honest, we're all a bundle of strengths and weaknesses, and our children see both. It can only help your parenting to take some time to reflect on the messages that are being communicated by your life to ensure that the positives create more vivid pictures for your children than anything negative.

OUR EXPERIENCE HAS BEEN THAT THE FAITH CONVERSATIONS WE HAD WITH OUR CHILDREN HAD TO BE VALIDATED BY OUR LIFESTYLE. "

TAKE ACTION

Go back to pages 30-31 and write below the three actions that received your lowest ranking. Then, write an action plan for improving in those specific areas. It's okay for it to be a small step — as long as you start somewhere.

1. _____ My starting action: _____

2. _____ My starting action: _____

3. _____ My starting action: _____

Assuming it's important to you, what can you work on — beginning today — to pass on your faith to your children?

_____

_____

Is there someone in your life you can look toward and learn from who could become a role model to you for parenting? If so, how might you pursue a deeper relationship with this person?

_____

_____

_____

_____

Are you encouraging or discouraging your children to have other caring adults in their lives? What are you doing to help facilitate other quality adults connecting with your children?

_____

_____

_____

List some names of people that your children would benefit from being around:

_____

_____

_____

_____

_____

_____

LET'S BE HONEST, WE'RE ALL A BUNDLE OF STRENGTHS AND WEAKNESSES, **AND OUR CHILDREN SEE BOTH.**

 If you have not already done so, please watch the "Strong Belief & 24/7 Role Model" Discussion Video with Doug & Cathy.

ACTION 3
ENCOURAGING WORDS

ACTION 3 **ENCOURAGING WORDS**

Intentional Parents regularly use words that are positive and life-giving.

Watch the "Encouraging Words & Genuine Affection" Teaching Video prior to reading this chapter.

Encouragement is one of our deepest cravings. Here's how you know if your child needs encouraging words: if she is breathing, encouragement is required.

Good words are like food for one's soul. Unfortunately most children are starving for positive, affirming, life-giving words. Whoever made up the fable, "Sticks and stones will break my bones, but words will never hurt me," was an idiot. Words hold much more power than we want to admit. Intentional Parents learn how to use their words to nourish their children.

Words are powerful and memorable. We remember words that are pointed and positive. We also remember words that are sharp and negative.

The human brain processes physical and emotional pain in a similar way. This means that negative words can literally hurt and cause pain since our brains perceive little difference. Just as physical wounds leave scars, so do the emotional wounds caused by the misuse of words. This is consistent with what the Scriptures say:

"Thoughtless words cut deeply like a thrusting sword, but the speech of the wise is a healing balm." Proverbs 12:18 (Voice)

"The words of the wicked are like a murderous ambush, but the words of the godly save lives."
Proverbs 12:6 (NLT)

A Quick-Fix Parent doesn't give thought to their words and allows emotion (what is being felt in the moment) to dictate their words. Consider some of these cutting/wicked statements:

Sarcasm: "Well, look who decided to grace us with her presence, and only ten minutes late this time."

Name-calling: "I can't believe you acted like such an idiot in front of our guests."

Disgust: "Wipe that stupid-looking grin off your face."

Shaming: "I think boys would be more attracted to you if you lost a few pounds."

Swearing: "You are such a dumb *#@&*!"

These are examples of mean-spirited, wounding words. But words can also be wounding that appear to be neutral or benign. Misguided words — even if not accompanied by a mean spirit or negative tone — can have a negative impact on a young life. The following examples are words that literally have the power to shape a child's life direction. Chances are good you've seen this displayed when a parent repeatedly uses words to describe their child:

- he's shy
- she's awkward
- he's not very coordinated
- she's not good with people
- he's my wild child

On the surface, these statements don't appear wicked, but words accompanied by negative modifiers infiltrate a child's mind and heart, and it's not uncommon for the child to become the person they are being described as. Words have the ability to shape a child in positive and negative ways.

ACTIVITY:
ENCOURAGING WORDS

What negative words can you still recall from your childhood?

_____

_____

_____

Why do you think those words are seared into your memory?

_____

_____

_____

Quick-Fix Parents don't stop to think about the damage looming behind their words. They just say whatever is on their minds or in their hearts. Their impulsive, spoken-darts shoot out verbal destruction that shames, manipulates, and destroys.

Think about your own arsenal of words that you tend to rely on when you're frustrated or angry. What words or terms or phrases would someone find you using if they were to record how you talk to your kids? Write them down so you can look at them from a new point of view. List them here:

_____

_____

_____

Why might these words be damaging to your child?

_____

_____

_____

Intentional Parents understand that words are powerful, and their choice of words can either build confidence in their children or destroy their hope.

ACTIVITY:
ENCOURAGING WORDS (CONT'D)

Let's pause and take an assessment of the words you typically use when talking to your child during different scenarios.

I JUST SAY WHATEVER I FEEL				I'LL TYPICALLY PAUSE AND CONSIDER MY WORDS				I AM ALWAYS CAREFUL AND WEIGH MY WORDS	

When I'm angry

| 1 | 2 | 3 | 4 | 5 | 6 | 7 | 8 | 9 | 10 |

When my child interrupts me

| 1 | 2 | 3 | 4 | 5 | 6 | 7 | 8 | 9 | 10 |

When I want to stop my child's behavior

| 1 | 2 | 3 | 4 | 5 | 6 | 7 | 8 | 9 | 10 |

When my child questions me or my decisions

| 1 | 2 | 3 | 4 | 5 | 6 | 7 | 8 | 9 | 10 |

When I am busy

| 1 | 2 | 3 | 4 | 5 | 6 | 7 | 8 | 9 | 10 |

When my child is rude to me or others

| 1 | 2 | 3 | 4 | 5 | 6 | 7 | 8 | 9 | 10 |

When my child doesn't pay attention to instructions

| 1 | 2 | 3 | 4 | 5 | 6 | 7 | 8 | 9 | 10 |

When I'm tired or hungry

| 1 | 2 | 3 | 4 | 5 | 6 | 7 | 8 | 9 | 10 |

As you reflect on the use of your words, what comes to mind?

_____

How might you become more intentional with your words?

_____

Please know that we're not suggesting that your words can't ever be directive or negative. Of course, there are times when you need to use words that are direct, instructional, and necessary.

In our own family we learned that as a result of being intentional and positive with our words, any variation of speech and/or tone would trigger a defensive and negative response from our kids.

I (Doug) can remember a time when our daughter said, "Dad, Mom was yelling at me." I was within earshot in the other room during the "yelling," and I heard Cathy's voice — it was not raised. But, was Mom peppy, happy, or positive? No. She was direct. Her words were pointed and necessary.

Cathy was not alone in being misunderstood. She remembers our son telling her, "Dad was getting on my case about taking out the trash." As parents, when we would hear this type of comment we would just look at each other and smile. We weren't getting on his case; rather, we were making a case for when he needed to do something.

If you're constantly "on their case," you are conditioning your children to avoid you. Just like you, they would rather be with people who enjoy them and speak kindly to them. Intentional Parents need to constantly ask, "What's the most encouraging way to say it?"

Intentional Parents make a plan or script for situations they know will appear. Think through how you will respond with respect to your child when:

- He is late getting ready for school.
- The cleanliness of her room doesn't meet your standards.
- You have asked him to do something and he didn't.

All parents face situations that trigger anger and test patience. It's going to happen, and it can happen often. But, when you're ready for it and intentional with your response, you are a wise and caring parent.

Let's consider some specific examples of how the same instructions can be given with both negative and positive words.

Negative instruction sounds like this:

> *"How many times do I have to tell you to put your backpack away?"*

> *"You are totally irresponsible. Are you always going to forget your lunch?"*

> *"Stop it. Why are you being so stupid? You are driving me crazy!"*

A positive use of words might sound like this:

> *"I'd like for you to please put your backpack away. I'd also appreciate it if you would do that every night before dinner."*

> *"One of my dreams for you is to develop responsibility. If you forget your lunch again, you'll need to go hungry until you get home. I love you too much to save you from opportunities to grow!"*

> *"Buddy, I'd like you to stop doing that please. If you choose to continue, there will be an appropriate consequence."*

ACTIVITY:
ENCOURAGING WORDS

As you read those opposing scenarios, what goes through your mind? Does it seem realistic for you to use positive words when you're frustrated?

_____

_____

If you are really honest, which home sounds more like yours — the negative or the positive examples? How might your children respond to this same question?

_____

_____

What do you think would need to change within yourself to be a parent who uses positive words?

_____

_____

Using words that are positive and life-giving will require some practice. You may need to develop a new vocabulary as well as some new coping skills for when you're frustrated and angry. As difficult as this might be, over time your positive words will result in positive impact.

Write a response to the following scenarios that don't use painful words, but clearly and calmly communicate what you want your kids to hear.

CLEANING THE ROOM

GETTING ALONG WITH SIBLINGS

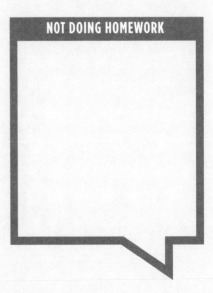
NOT DOING HOMEWORK

If the use of encouraging words was not modeled to you, it will definitely be a more difficult action. It may be as challenging as learning a foreign language. Becoming fluent in encouragement requires discipline, focus, and hard work. Here's the good news: you have the opportunity to break free from what you missed out on and not repeat that destructive cycle or pass it to your children. Don't allow your past to define and determine your present. Your kids need you to grow strong in this area.

As you work to become an Intentional Parent with your words, we feel it's necessary to warn you not to expect encouragement to be returned by your child. We know you want it; we did too. You pour out so much love that of course you want some of it returned. We've heard parents say, "He never says anything nice to me, so I'm just giving him his own treatment." When we hear this we simply remind parents that no matter how frustrated they become, they need to be the adult and keep pouring on encouragement. In our experience, usually a child will receive positive words (whether he returns them or not) and then learn how to use his own words more constructively as he grows into adulthood.

If you were able to peer into the future when all of your children are young adults, you would be able to see them deploying encouragement to you when they have a fully developed emotional vocabulary. Right now, they don't… but those days are coming quickly. If you keep that in mind, you won't have to live with constant disappointment. Remember, parenting and perseverance are synonymous terms.

WE'VE HEARD PARENTS SAY, "HE NEVER SAYS ANYTHING NICE TO ME, **SO I'M JUST GIVING HIM HIS OWN TREATMENT."**

◈ ENCOURAGE TOWARD YOUR END GAME

Revisit page 21 and be reminded of what you wrote when you thought about what you want for you child when this particular time expires: 6,570 days… 936 weeks… 216 months.

If you really believe your words matter over time, then your words need to become intentionally directed toward your end game. This requires some advanced thinking, but let's consider our example of wanting our children to possess confidence, character, compassion, conviction, and competence (see page 22). We had to ask ourselves, "Are we using words that are encouraging those qualities?"

Consider some examples:

"	Regardless of whether you hit a homerun or strike out in today's game, I want you to know that I love watching you play and just be you!	**CONFIDENCE**
"	"I'm amazed at how patient you were with your little brother. Way to go!"	**CHARACTER**
"	I love when you tell me what you learned about Jesus during Sunday School.	**CONVICTION**
"	It was really kind of you to choose to serve your mom when she wasn't feeling well.	**COMPASSION**
"	I watched you solve that problem with your sister all by yourself, and I was amazed by your ability to think that one through.	**COMPETENCE**

Bottom line: Your words are way too powerful to not give them considerable thought.

This entire concept of an Intentional Parent using encouraging words is one of the more difficult actions in this workbook. On a typical day we'll speak thousands of words and, depending on our moods and emotions, our discernment filters may not be working that well.

Parents must learn to hold up the mirror and look within themselves to see that word actually originate from the depth of the heart. Good words come from a good heart. Ba words come from a bad heart. You can't say, "I didn't mean to say that!" What's mor accurate is that you didn't want it to be heard. You meant to say it because it was brewin in your heart.

Jesus said it like this:

> *"A good person produces good words from a good heart, and an evil person produces evil word from an evil heart. Matthew 12:35 (NLT)*

This means that if we're to become proficient at this specific action, we might requir some heart surgery.

In our own marriage and parenting, when we began to understand the teachings of Jesu and put our faith in Him and His ways, our marriage changed. Our parenting changec Actually, everything changed! God's Spirit invaded our lives and transformed our chai acter. If I (Doug) am really honest, when I became a parent, I wasn't ready to face m selfishness. I thought I faced it when I got married, but that was nothing compared t having children. Children don't leave you for several hours to go to work — actually, the don't ever leave you alone. Ever. Parenting pressed against my comfort and, on my ow power, I wasn't strong enough to be the Intentional Parent my kids needed. I needed Jesu to change my heart.

Everything powerful and good within relationships has a direct connection to one's hear A new or renewed heart may be needed for you to speak encouraging words on a regula basis.

No technique, no plan, no relationship strategies will really matter that much if you mis the bigger picture of God's love for you.

"Follow God's example, therefore, as dearly loved children…" Ephesians 5:1 (NIV)

You are God's dearly loved child. That Scripture doesn't say: "Follow God's example as the ones God tolerates." Or, "the ones with whom God is mostly disappointed." No! We are told that we are God's dearly loved children.

We are confident we have some solid parenting ideas in this workbook that are practical and helpful! But, if you somehow skip the critical truth that God calls you his "dearly loved children," then all of the best help in the world will still come up short. You will parent from a broken, wounded, or wrong identity.

Intentional Parents are those who recognize they are loved dearly and are capable of dearly loving. They go to bed knowing their God sings over them.

"He will rejoice over you with joyful songs." Zephaniah 3:17b (NLT)

TAKE ACTION

Write down the names of your children, and (next to their names) write out what benefit they may receive from constant encouragement. Next, list some specific areas of your children's lives that you think require the most encouragement right now, such as identity, friendships, character, etc.

NAME	BENEFIT OF ENCOURAGEMENT	NEEDED RIGHT NOW

Use the next page to begin thinking of your action steps to make encouragement a regular part of your parenting routine.

We believe you can learn to do this and do it well! And, it will make a huge difference in the hearts of your children.

HOW CAN I ENCOURAGE?

DAILY	
WEEKLY	
MONTHLY	

Please watch the "Encouraging Words & Genuine Affection" Discussion Video with Doug & Cathy.

ACTION 4
GENUINE AFFECTION

ACTION 4 **GENUINE AFFECTION**

Intentional Parents liberally give affection.

 If you have not already done so, watch the "Encouraging Words & Genuine Affection" Teaching Video prior to reading this chapter.

Anyone who has ever taken one class in psychology, sociology, or child development has learned about the desperate need children have for affection. All of us, from the time we're born, experience what social scientists refer to as "skin hunger." We are hungry for touch! We need affection — and that hunger must be fed in appropriate ways or its deficit will lead to emotional imbalance.

Study after study reveals that affection actually helps shape a child's brain. For babies, the part of the brain that is involved in controlling emotions, paying attention to others, and expressing empathy is not developed automatically. It develops in response to the baby's social experiences.

As children age, those who have felt physical love and warmth from their parents show higher self-esteem, better communication with their parents, and fewer psychological and behavioral problems. On the flipside, insufficient affection can lead to feelings of alienation, hostility, aggression, lower self-esteem, and anti-social and risky behaviors.

Unfortunately, disturbing data suggests that parents typically withdraw from expressing affection as children get older. They rely more on their words to communicate rather than touch.

Males are already at a disadvantage with affection. Statistically and stereotypically women have a much easier time showing affection to children than men do.

This could be why you rarely ever see a child get hurt and run into the house yelling "Dad!" Why? Easy. Dad doesn't care. That's not the truth of course, but Dad is often better with his words… or at least he thinks he is. Dad might say:

- "Don't cry."
- "Shake it off."
- "You'll be fine; just put some ice on it. And, while you're at the freezer, why don't you scoop me some ice cream."

Yes, children need positive words, but they also need physical affection in good times and in bad times. One of the characteristics that emotionally healthy children have in common is that they have been given proper affection — and lots of it.

We understand the potential hurdles some parents have toward affection. We've heard these types of excuses at our seminars:

- "Affection wasn't modeled to me."
- "It's just not my personality to be touchy-feely."
- "I was abused as a child, and I struggle with this whole subject.'"

If you find yourself nodding in agreement with any of those statements, we are so sorry for your past. The truth is that we've all got different and difficult hurdles to clear in order to become Intentional Parents. We must face those hurdles, figure them out, and move forward before we wound our kids with a lack of affection.

ACTIVITY:
GENUINE AFFECTION

How was affection expressed and modeled to you when you were growing up?

_____

_____

Which one of these statements best applies to you?

- ☐ My parents were overly affectionate.
- ☐ My parents were comfortable with affection, but not overly liberal with it.
- ☐ My parents were better with their words than affection.
- ☐ I don't remember my parents being very affectionate.
- ☐ My parents were distant with their words and affection.

Looking back at your parents' use of affection and your current use, are you more like them or less like them?

Evaluate how you would rate yourself as an affectionate parent. Next to each of the physical actions you could take toward your child below, give yourself a letter grade on each one:

> **A = Comfortable**
> **B = Easy to do, but not comfortable**
> **C = I can do it, but it's not natural**
> **D = Uncomfortable**
> **F = Not a chance**

_____ Back rub

_____ Hug

_____ Tight embrace

_____ Hold hands

_____ Dance

_____ Lay in bed talking

_____ Kiss on the cheek

_____ Kiss on the lips

_____ Cuddle

_____ Wrestle

_____ Look deeply into eyes while holding the face

_____ Snuggle while watching TV

_____ Hold on lap

ACTIVITY:
GENUINE AFFECTION (CONT'D)

Looking over your affection grades, do you see any themes in how you scored?

_____

_____

Why do you think affection is easy (or difficult) for you?

_____

_____

Write your response to the following statement: *Affection is a tangible proof of love. Caring, appropriate touch is the exclamation point in "I love you!"*

_____

_____

_____

_____

_____

_____

_____

_____

_____

_____

_____

_____

_____

_____

You may need to practice affection by taking baby steps until your comfort level increases. Even if this is tough for you, you've got to understand that your children need to be held, hugged, wrestled, and kissed. Daily. Regularly. Liberally. Don't pass over this chapter and think, "I'm pretty good at the others… the kids will be okay if this isn't my strength."

It may not be your strength, but that doesn't mean you can't become more comfortable with it. We're not asking you to go hug strangers; we're begging you to feed your child's skin hunger and to understand that he or she is always hungry for more genuine expressions of love from Mom and Dad.

WHAT IF MY TEENAGER DOESN'T WANT AFFECTION?

With older children, affection can become a lot more difficult. That's why Quick-Fix Parents give up when their attempts at affection are met with resistance. As children get older, the expressions of affection may need to change, but the regularity of affection shouldn't. In order to keep up with the frequency, you have to be more assertive and intentional.

When our kids were little, they would happily come into the house and hug and kiss us and tell us stories about their time outside. That stopped during late elementary years. When they quit initiating affection and conversation, that became our signal that we needed to step it up and be even more intentional.

AS CHILDREN GET OLDER, THE EXPRESSIONS OF AFFECTION MAY NEED TO CHANGE, **BUT THE REGULARITY OF AFFECTION SHOULDN'T.**

Parents of pre-teens and teenagers, please hear this loud and clear: you've got to POUR IT ON! When puberty hits, most parents back off with the affection because their kids suddenly start acting weird (demon possessed might be too exaggerated, but you get the point).

They roll their eyes, and tell you you're weird and embarrassing to them. Talk about irony! You will find yourself wanting to say, "Oh, I'm embarrassing to YOU? Really? Have you looked in the mirror and seen the way you dress?" (But since you've read chapter three on encouragement you only think those thoughts and then choose to use different words. Right?)

When your kids are in middle school, they most likely will want you drop them off around the corner instead of risking that their friends might see you and actually think they have parents. Most children go through a stage of development when they try to discover their identity apart from their parents. While this is painful, it's also normal. You must fight the temptation to take it so personally.

THEY DON'T WANT YOU TO BE AFFECTIONATE, BUT THEY NEED YOU TO BE. "

If you take their disengagement personally, you'll separate yourself from them at a time where they need you to be a secure, caring figure in their lives. Let's be clear: they don't want you to be affectionate, but they need you to be. So, instead of that embarrassing hug in the school parking lot, give a gentle, lingering arm squeeze or leg pat as they leave the car accompanied by the words, "I love you!"

Intentional Parents need to respect that preteens and teens are trying to figure out their independence in front of their friends. But, at home, you've got to pour it on. Again, they may resist you — that's part of growing up. If you stop now it will be tougher to restart when they have gone through the searching for independence stage. You've got to be the adult in the relationship and not be hurt by their disengagement.

They will give the impression that they don't need you or want you. It's not true. They have deep needs for parent involvement in their life; they just don't know how to adequately communicate those needs and desires. Remember, their emotional vocabulary isn't fully developed.

If you push those opportunities for connection away, eventually they'll go away completely. We've seen it over and over: the kids who don't get appropriate affection at home will seek it out in other ways. And, unfortunately, our culture has a lot of options for physical affection outside the home.

Start somewhere! That's the key with everything connected to Intentional Parenting. Something is better than nothing. Remember, 216 months is counting down. Your affection over time will make a difference.

IF YOU TAKE THEIR DISENGAGEMENT PERSONALLY, YOU'LL SEPARATE YOURSELF FROM THEM AT A TIME **WHERE THEY NEED YOU TO BE A SECURE, CARING FIGURE IN THEIR LIVES.**

TAKE ACTION

It may seem counterintuitive to plan out your affection, but it may be what's needed. Spend some time below thinking about how you will provide affection to each of your children.

My kids: _____

Ages: _____

On a scale of 1-10 how easy (1) — to — hard (10) is it to give each child affection?

| 1 | 2 | 3 | 4 | 5 | 6 | 7 | 8 | 9 | 10 |

What is one way you can begin today to express affection to each child's unique age and personality?

_____

_____

If you're at the blessed stage of your parenting where your children still openly express affection, you can begin to teach them to expect your affection. We told our kids when they were little that hugging and kissing is just something our family does, and there is no way around it.

Practice affection with your kids this week. Pour it on! Put your arm around them as you walk out the door. Sit close to them and touch legs. If all of this is too uncomfortable, pretend to trip and just fall on them (we're kidding… sort of).

If you have not already done so, please watch the "Encouraging Words & Genuine Affection" Discussion Video with Doug & Cathy.

ACTION 5
CONSISTENT PRESENCE

ACTION 5 **CONSISTENT PRESENCE**

> *Intentional Parents* make sacrifices in order to be consistently present.

Watch the "Consistent Presence & Peaceful Home" Teaching Video prior to reading this chapter.

We have had countless conversations with our grown children and their friends about their growing up years, and it's astounding how often the concept of parental presence surfaces as they replay their childhoods.

- *"It meant so much to me that you were always at my games."*

- *"I'm so grateful that you were home for me during my difficult adolescent years."*

- *"I never knew where my parents were going to be."*

- *"I lacked the confidence that I saw in other kids who knew their parents were available and present in their lives."*

Of course it's impossible for parents to be present all the time. That's why we didn't title this chapter "Constantly Present" or "Don't-cut-the-umbilical-cord Presence." Consistency is the key with the gift of presence. In order to be present for children, parents must make sacrifices so they can be there as often as possible. This is a hard truth for many parents to embrace, but as we've said before, parenting is synonymous with sacrifice.

PRESENCE IS BIG!

Your presence makes a statement. Presence communicates that you care about your child's world. It sends the message that she matters to you and you're willing to make her world an important priority in your world. Your presence in her life adds to her foundation of confidence.

Presence doesn't just happen — it requires intentional actions. You've got to plan, strategize, and sacrifice.

Intentional Parents must strongly believe that every "yes" they say to something outside of their primary parenting role becomes a "no" to their family. It's harsh, but true. You can't say "yes" to everything and everyone and give your children your leftover time, then simply hope they'll turn out alright because they're young and seem resilient. An Intentional Parent doesn't use hope as a primary parenting strategy.

PRESENCE DOESN'T JUST HAPPEN—IT REQUIRES INTENTIONAL ACTIONS. YOU'VE GOT TO PLAN, STRATEGIZE, AND SACRIFICE. "

Do you see any common factors impacting your ability to be present?
Check the ones that apply:

_____ Work/Job

_____ Priorities

_____ Overall too busy

_____ Not on my radar

_____ Doing "good" somewhere else

_____ Not really interested in their interests

_____ Lazy

_____ Preoccupied

_____ My spouse had it covered

_____ Other:

Earlier in this workbook, we discussed the concept of time moving quickly (remember: your child's 18th birthday makes up 6,570 days, or 936 weeks, or only 216 months). This is never more real than when we talk about presence.

Many parents view this principle of presence as a waste of time because it's difficult at times to see tangible results. It's very normal to wonder, "Does it even matter that I'm here? It doesn't feel like my children know I'm alive let alone at their [insert anything here]! Isn't quality time more important than quantity of time?"

Dads, I (Doug) know this is tough! Especially with babies. When my kids were infants, I always thought there were more productive things to do than sit on the floor and play blocks. But all that baby time that doesn't seem productive is building a foundation for you and your kids to grow into a relationship as they get older.

Which one of these options is most appealing to you?

____ I'd rather be known as a parent who spends quality time, less often.
____ I'm all about quantity time — the more, the better.
____ At this point, I'll take whatever time I can get with my kids.
____ My kids are of the age where time with them doesn't seem very productive.
____ My kids are of the age where they seem like they couldn't care less if I spend time with them.
____ Other (explain).

Being present for a child is a challenge to one's priorities and selfishness.

Our experience has been that the parents who subscribe to the quality over quantity time theory either don't understand the power connected to being a present parent, or more likely, they're trying to ease the guilt they feel for not being there.

An exception to this is a single parent: if you are a struggling single parent doing everything you can to put food on the table, you are heroic. We honor you for working so hard to hold things together, and we believe God will credit your hard work and your children will someday recognize it and call you blessed.

Single parents: let's pause and acknowledge your hard work and all that you are doing right. Make a list of some of the things that you're currently doing that are clearly sacrificial.

_____

_____

_____

_____

_____

What kids won't appreciate are parents who aren't working just to survive, but who are over-working in order to drive fancy cars, live in nicer houses, and stroke their own egos. These parents have a tendency to blame their kids' habits and activities as the reason they need to work so much. Blame is easier than taking a look inward at what might be the real motives for working so much. Again, that's what Quick-Fix Parents do — they take the easier route. Casting blame is simple and allows parents to feel better about themselves.

An Intentional Parent recognizes that kids need their presence more than the presents their work affords.

This concept of presence is a strong theme throughout the Bible. Think about it…

GOD'S PRESENCE BROUGHT EVERYTHING INTO EXISTENCE.

"In the beginning God created the heavens and the earth." Genesis 1:1 (NLT)

GOD'S PRESENCE INVADED THE EARTH IN HUMAN FORM — JESUS.

"So the Word [Jesus] became human and made His home among us." John 1:14a (NLT)

THE PRESENCE OF GOD THROUGH THE HOLY SPIRIT

For those of us who have a relationship with God made available through Jesus' sacrifice on the cross, the resulting promise is that we possess the presence of God through the Holy Spirit.

"I pray that from His glorious, unlimited resources He will empower you with inner strength through His Spirit. Then Christ will make His home in your hearts as you trust in Him." Ephesians 3:16-17a (NLT)

Here's more good news: it's through the help of God's Spirit and His unlimited resources that parents can make the sacrifices needed to become better at being present in their child's life.

GOD CREATED US TO BE PRESENT WITH ONE ANOTHER.

We aren't intended to live alone, and the truth that's lived out every day is that we become better people when we are with others. Our faith can be strengthened by the presence of others in our lives.

> *"Then the Lord God said, "It is not good for the man to be alone. I will make a helper who is just right for him." Genesis 2:18 (NLT)*

> *"When we get together, I want to encourage you in your faith, but I also want to be encouraged by yours." Romans 1:12 (NLT)*

As you can see, presence is a big deal to God. It's one of the primary ways that love is expressed.

CASTING BLAME IS SIMPLE AND ALLOWS PARENTS TO FEEL BETTER ABOUT THEMSELVES.

ACTIVITY:
PRESENCE IS BIG!

If children are a gift from God, could it be that God created you to be a present parent? What does that responsibility feel like to you in this moment?

_____

_____

_____

_____

Do you believe in God's profound presence in your own life? Why or why not?

_____

_____

_____

_____

How do these verses strike you personally — even outside of your role as a parent — regarding God's presence for you? Why might that be important for your own faith development?

_____

_____

_____

_____

How would you like God to answer your prayer to be more sacrificial and present?

_____

_____

_____

_____

◈ PERCEIVED PRESENCE

At our seminars, when we speak about this idea of presence, there is always at least on parent who wants us to know they're at home a lot. They'll say something like, "I wor from home." Or, "I'm a stay-at-home mom/dad."

Our response is usually, "That's great… what a fabulous opportunity! But, being presen is bigger than you working from home."

We explain that the deeper question is, "Is just your body around the house, or is you heart available too?" In other words, "Your kids may realize you're around, but do they really believe you're available?" There's a big difference.

Sometimes, just being physically present is not enough. Parents who may be nearby bu who are not emotionally invested or responsive tend to raise children who are more dis tressed and less engaged with their play or activities. A study investigating the connectior between parental investment and children's competence suggests that the emotional in volvement of parents really does matter and affects the outcome of their children's emo tional competence and regulation.[3]

Perception is fact in the eyes of the beholder. You might be a stay-at-home parent, but if you're hiding behind your work or stuck in an office or glued to your laptop, and your child's perception is that you're too busy for her, then her truth is that you are unavailable

---

3. Bethel Moges and Kristi Weber, Parental Influence on the Emotional Development of Children
https://my.vanderbilt.edu/developmentalpsychologyblog/2014/05/parental-influence-on-the-emotional-development-of-children/

ACTIVITY:
PERCEIVED PRESENCE

EMOTIONALLY PRESENT TEST

Your child's perception of your presence is something to consider.

How emotionally available are you when you're around your children?

NOT AT ALL									I'M IN THE ZONE

1	2	3	4	5	6	7	8	9	10

How might your spouse answer this question about you?

_____

What's something you're currently doing for yourself that may be taking too much time away from your kids?

Personal: _____

Career: _____

What might need to be reevaluated in these areas of your life in order to be more present?

_____

_____

Could your children be sending you any clues about what they think of your presence? Think deeply. Does anything come to mind?

_____

_____

How do you respond to the following statement: "Missing something in your child's world should be the exception rather than the rule."

_____

_____

If you're a sports parent (or something similar where you observe your child playing and/or competing), we encourage you to be your child's cheerleader rather than his coach. Stop instructing him from the sidelines or coaching him in the car ride on the way home. If you want to say something you think is constructive, wait until 48 hours after the game or event. Your "in the moment" coaching is often interpreted as judging. We know you have his best interest in mind, and your motives are to help him, but remember: perception is fact. He has a coach. He needs a cheerleader who is happy to be present... win or lose... succeed or fail. Learn to play that role well and your presence will be greatly valued.

◈ REMOVING THE DIGITAL LEASHES

One of the biggest hurdles toward becoming a present parent is dealing with one's own electronic dependency. When your head is faced down and your eyes are glued to a small mobile screen, you're not present. Social scientists have developed the term "technoference" to describe habits and actions that involve technology (techno) and its harmful impact on relationships (ference). Intentional Parents figure out ways to make sure mobile devices don't wound their primary relationships.

Suggestion: Ditch the phone when you're in the car with your child. Yes, use your phone when your kids aren't present, but when they are in

your car keep it off. Be present. Your children are trapped with you. You can take advantage of that time and talk, sing, play games, make jokes, be present. If not, you will train your children that cars are made for device use, and as soon as they get their own device, it will be much easier for them to be consumed by the screen than to be engaged with conversation — conversation that you'll really want as they get older.

Suggestion: Develop a media-free home zone. You don't need to become Amish, buy a buggy, and flee from all things electric. Instead we encourage you to have some boundaries, guidelines, and rules when it comes to the consumption of media. There ought to be times when you're totally available to your family and unplugged from your devices, and your kids are too. We feel strongly that this same suggestion applies when you're at restaurants or out as a family.

I (Doug) co-authored a workbook for parents titled, *Should I Just SMASH My Kid's Phone?*[4] Because most parents are going crazy over their child's phone use, but few parents have developed their own media rules. Unfortunately, the do-as-I-say-not-as-I-do style of parenting is not only Quick-Fix Parenting, it's totally ineffective. Parents must be willing to figure out their own media habits first. Personally, we believe it's foolish to provide children with a phone without establishing user guidelines. Please do your homework. Develop an intentional strategy so that you and your child don't disappear behind an electronic device.

WHERE ARE YOU ON YOUR OWN MOBILE USE?

I DON'T EVEN OWN A PHONE	I USE IT WHEN NECESSARY	OKAY, SO I'M ON IT A LOT!
1 2 3	4 5 6 7	8 9 10

What media boundaries need to be established in your life so you can be more present with your children?

_____

_____

_____

_____

4. *Should I Just SMASH my Kid's Cell Phone?* is available at DougFields.com

TAKE ACTION

Write down some ideas that might be helpful for a media-free zone within your home. What are ideas that would be…

Realistic and easy to implement:

_____

_____

This would be difficult, but we could do it:

_____

_____

Probably not a chance of this happening, but I know if I did it I would definitely be more present:

_____

_____

What are two new "rules" and/or "guidelines" you can set for yourself to start being a more present parent? (You don't need to announce these to your family and seek martyrdom credit… just be there.)

_____

_____

Where is one place you could start showing up that would be a good surprise to your kids?

_____

_____

_____

As we close this chapter, write your response to the following statement: "Being fully present sends the message: 'You matter to me!' "

_____

_____

_____

Take some time to make a plan to spend time with each of your kids in an individual manner. Make it a goal to do this with each of your kids this week.

NAME	AGE	HURDLE TO SPENDING TIME TOGETHER	ACTIONS TO TAKE

Please watch the "Consistent Presence & Peaceful Home" Discussion Video with Doug & Cathy.

ACTION 6
PEACEFUL HOME

Intentional Parents create a shelter
from the storm.

 If you have not already done so, watch the "Consistent Presence & Peaceful Home" Teaching Video prior to reading this chapter.

Kids need a peaceful home in order to help them escape the chaos that encircles their world. This chaos can include choosing friends, pleasing friends, avoiding friends, bullying, peer pressure, school, grades, assignments they don't understand, riding the bus, and making many daily decisions. It's not easy being a kid these days.

As our children entered their elementary school years, we discussed a fictitious scenario where our kids would come home from school, throw open the door, quickly slam it shut behind them, lean against the door, slide down it, sit on the floor, smile over the fact that they were in a safe place, and then shout, "I'm home!" with a feeling of relief. While it never happened exactly that way, we tried to create a home where our kids would feel safe.

A peaceful home is a safe home.

The world of today's children and teenagers is often filled with painful battles. In addition to the stereotypical battles we mentioned above, they also battle body image comparisons every time they turn on the TV or pick up a magazine. These types of battles are unavoidable, but if a child knows she's going home to a safe, peaceful environment… she can better handle all the stress, pressure, comparisons, putdowns, and temptations that surround her life. She knows that pretty soon she'll be home — a place that is both peaceful and safe.

There is no such thing as a perfect home, but there can be peaceful homes.

Our house was often hectic! During our kids' teenage years it sometimes seemed more like New York's Grand Central Station than a peaceful sanctuary. There were kids coming and going, and it wasn't unusual for us to come home to complete strangers informing us that we were out of ice or hotdogs or toilet paper. One time our son's friend spilled something on the carpet, and as we walked in he was looking at the spill intently. He looked at us and said, "Mr. & Mrs. Fields, check this out! If you tilt your head slightly to the right and squint, that spill looks like the face of Jesus."

I (Cathy) said, "Jason, let's figure out a way to clean that up before Doug figures out a way for you to actually go meet Jesus right now."

There's no escaping the fact that we had an active, kid-oriented home. But, in the midst of all the movement, we intentionally strived for a peaceful home.

A peaceful home doesn't necessarily mean a quiet home, but a peaceful home does include:

- Discipline without screaming and yelling.
- Boundaries, but not too many rules.
- An environment that is welcoming to friends.
- Words of encouragement rather than critical comments.
- Warm and consistent affection.
- Parents who express love for one another and display a secure marriage.
- Freedom from being compared with siblings.
- A place where kids can be themselves and they don't have to pretend.
- A shame-free atmosphere.

ACTIVITY:
PEACEFUL HOME

Your turn. Place check marks in the boxes next to the ones that currently describe your home.

- ☐ Discipline without screaming and yelling.
- ☐ Boundaries, but not too many rules.
- ☐ An environment that is welcoming to friends.
- ☐ Words of encouragement rather than critical comments.
- ☐ Warm and consistent affection.
- ☐ Parents who express love for one another and display a secure marriage.
- ☐ Freedom from being compared with siblings.
- ☐ A place where kids can be themselves and they don't have to pretend.
- ☐ A shame-free atmosphere.

What is missing from the list above that you would add to bring about a peaceful home?

_____

_____

_____

In the long run, do you think your children will describe your house as a place of peace? Why or why not?

_____

_____

_____

When you reflect on the home you grew up in, can you think of anything your parents did to create a place of peace for you?

_____

_____

_____

ACTIVITY:
PEACEFUL HOME (CONT'D)

What about chaos? Do you remember what they did/didn't do that led to home being chaotic?

_____

_____

_____

Can you see yourself bringing any positive or negative patterns from your family of origin into your current family? If so, which ones?

_____

_____

_____

We are not naive about many family situations. Your home may be complete chaos right now. You are trying your best, but peace is out of your control. Your marriage may be suffering and your children sense it, and it creates in them a sense of fear and insecurity. There may be financial stress or illness or extended family pressure, and peace doesn't seem realistic in your future. We encounter this often when we talk to families. You may need more than a parenting workbook to discover the peace you desperately need. You may need counseling and insight from those outside your circle of stress who can provide objective insight that can really help you. Don't be afraid to get help; there is no shame in seeking guidance and counseling.

Let's dig deeper into three from our list on page 84:

- Freedom from being compared to siblings.
- A place where kids can be themselves and they don't have to pretend.
- A shame-free atmosphere.

All three of these contribute to your child feeling peace in your home through acceptance. Intentional Parents are very purposeful in communicating acceptance to each of their children.

Your children may be very different from one another. You may have a "mini-me," and your spouse may also have a "mini-me" that is more like him or her than you. You may also have a child that causes you to think, "I have no idea where he came from!"

Throughout various life stages your kids will battle the question, "Am I going to be accepted here?" That question even moves into adulthood. Intentional Parents must wisely allow their kids to become who they were created to be.

You may or may not have a future professional athlete on your hands or a famous musician or actress like you always dreamed your child would be. You may need to let go of some of your own dreams and stop pushing your children to be who you want them to be, and instead accept and appreciate them for being people with their own uniqueness and giftedness — even if those gifts don't match your hopes and dreams.

You may have always wanted a child who is a multi-sport athlete, but you have a computer genius instead. You may have dreamed about a musical prodigy, and your kid has no rhythm and can't play chopsticks.

Children need to be accepted by their parents — the most important people in their lives. Acceptance builds confidence in your children. They will take greater risks at things they love and possibly find great success. Acceptance in your home is an instrumental action in having a peaceful home.

ACTIVITY:
PEACEFUL HOME

Child's Name:_____

A unique, quality he/she possesses:_____

How can I best communicate acceptance?_____

Child's Name:_____

A unique, quality he/she possesses:_____

How can I best communicate acceptance?_____

Child's Name:_____

A unique, quality he/she possesses:_____

How can I best communicate acceptance?_____

One factor that seems to keep peace at a distance is when parents make their parenting decisions based on how others might view them as parents. Basically, they parent from a place of fear or anticipation of others' opinions of them as parents. We call that Performance Parenting, and it quenches any movement toward peace.

If you parent in order to look good or you are overly concerned about how your kids make you look, then you are wounding your child. Or, you subtly pressure your kids to perform a certain way — with the thought that if they "succeed" then others will have a higher opinion of you... you're performing. Here's a warning to seriously consider: this type of insecure parenting will lead to trouble, kids who have major issues, and future therapy bills.

Seek help before your children are wounded any further. Don't fall into this Quick-Fix Parenting trap.

This type of parenting will not produce peace! It's a display of a parent's insecurity. Insecure parents create shame and pressure-filled environments that ultimately wound children.

 ## WHAT'S THE ANSWER?

To create a peace-filled home, you must become a peace-filled person. The Biblical word for peace is often translated "absence of war." To live as a peace-filled person means you aren't at war — you're not at war with God or others or even within yourself.

We realize that the word "war" might seem like too strong of a word. It may be, but the Bible teaches that because of our sinful nature we are separated from God. Sin is another way of saying that we choose to do things our own way instead of God's way. We are all born with this sin-nature, and when we do things our own way we become separated from God because God is holy and we're not.

The good news is that God made a way for this war to be won. It required Jesus to die on the cross and pay the price of our sin that we couldn't pay on our own. Because of what Jesus did on the cross, we can have a personal relationship with God.

"… and through him [Jesus] God reconciled everything to Himself. He [God] made peace with everything in heaven and on earth by means of Christ's blood on the cross." Colossians 1:20 (NLT)

How do you think you can personally experience peace as a result of Jesus' death on the cross?

_____

_____

_____

If you've never settled the relationship between you and God, we strongly suggest that you clearly and confidently investigate Jesus and see how He promises to bring peace. Again, if you want peace in your home, you need peace in your heart.

One of the great Biblical promises connected to having a personal relationship with God is that He promises the gift of His presence. This gift arrives through the Holy Spirit — the third person of the Trinity; God the Father, God the Son, God the Holy Spirit. One of the results of the Holy Spirit in your life is peace.

"...But letting the Holy Spirit control your mind leads to life and peace." Romans 8:6b (NLT)

With God's presence in our lives we can count on Him to help us transform our Quick-Fix Parenting into Intentional Parenting.

What do you think the word "control" means in the verse above?

_____

_____

Read the Galatians passage below: which of these fruits of God's Spirit is most attractive to you and why?

"But the Holy Spirit produces this kind of fruit in our lives: love, joy, peace, patience, kindness, goodness, faithfulness, gentleness, and self-control." Galatians 5:22-23a (NLT)

_____

_____

We suspect that for many parents, their answer to the question above may have been "peace." Because of God's brilliant plan (Jesus becoming human), His power (the resurrection), and His presence (the Holy Spirit), you have the potential to have peace within, peace with others, and ultimately you can become the initiator of peace within your home.

Your child needs a peaceful home, and that peaceful home starts in your heart.

TAKE ACTION

What are three actions you need to take to begin creating a peaceful home?

1. _____

2. _____

3. _____

Who is one person you know well who seems to model a peaceful heart? What is it specifically that he/she does to give you that impression? Could you initiate a conversation with this person and inquire about his/her "secrets"?

_____

_____

_____

_____

What might you do right away to develop a peaceful heart?

_____

_____

_____

 If you have not already done so, please watch the "Consistent Presence & Peaceful Home" Discussion Video with Doug & Cathy.

ACTION 7
DELICATE DISCIPLINE

ACTION 7 DELICATE DISCIPLINE

Intentional Parents view discipline as guidance with love.

Watch the "Delicate Discipline & Activate Responsibility" Teaching Video prior to reading this chapter.

When we see a child who isn't disciplined, we don't think less of the child. Actually, our immediate response is often compassion for the child. We feel sorry because the lack of discipline often points back to an absent parent, or even an unloving parent. We think, "Are the parents' inattentive? Clueless? Inexperienced? Unloving? What's the deal?"

Discipline is a sign of love. You can't fully love your child if you don't provide discipline. Love and discipline go together… both are acts of genuine care and concern.

Even God disciplines those He loves.

> *"For the Lord disciplines those he loves… If God doesn't discipline you as he does all of his children, it means that you are illegitimate and are not really his children at all."*
> *Hebrews 12:6a, 8 (NLT)*

> *"My child, don't reject the Lord's discipline, and don't be upset when He corrects you. For the Lord corrects those He loves, just as a father corrects a child in whom he delights."*
> *Proverbs 3: 11-12 (NLT)*

Did you notice the phrase: "a child in whom he delights"? What a beautiful term! Let' steal it for a moment — as parents we don't delight in discipline, rather we discipline those in whom we delight. Why? Because there's a bigger goal at play: wisdom.

> *"To discipline a child produces wisdom, but a mother is disgraced by an undisciplined child.*
> *Proverbs 29:15 (NLT)*

Intentional Parents discipline because they want their children to grow up to be wise competent, and thoughtful adults who possess the ability to make good decisions. These parents understand the long-term connection between decisions and consequences.

Quick-Fix Parents rely less on discipline and more on punishment. They punish thei children (often in anger) in order to stop their behavior and minimize their own inconvenience. Essentially, Quick-Fix Parents view discipline as an immediate means to change behavior.

Do you think your current discipline style is closer to Quick-Fix or Intentional Parenting right now? Why?

_____

_____

Our personal style with discipline was to avoid shame and yelling. We weren't 100 per cent perfect on this, but it was our goal to not humiliate our children by disciplining them in front of others. If we were in a public setting and discipline was necessary, we would take them out of the room and away from others to talk with them. By taking the time to remove the child from the setting, it gave us time to cool off and control our emotions. In addition, it reduced the shame our children would feel from others' eyes. This is a simple but powerful strategy.

YELLING DOESN'T WORK

As advocates for children we often beg parents not to discipline in anger. Long term, it's wounding to the child. Yelling, over time, proves to be ineffective. Please know that we're not suggesting that you never get angry. Not at all! We live in the real world. Instead, we're suggesting you become an Intentional Parent and learn to discipline without anger fueling your decisions. There's a big difference.

Study a fast-food restaurant play area and you'll see parents express their anger by yelling and slamming and smacking and yanking in order to tame their children's behavior. This type of discipline isn't done as an act of love; it's discipline in anger (or frustration) for the sake of compliance. It's a perfect example of Quick-Fix Parenting.

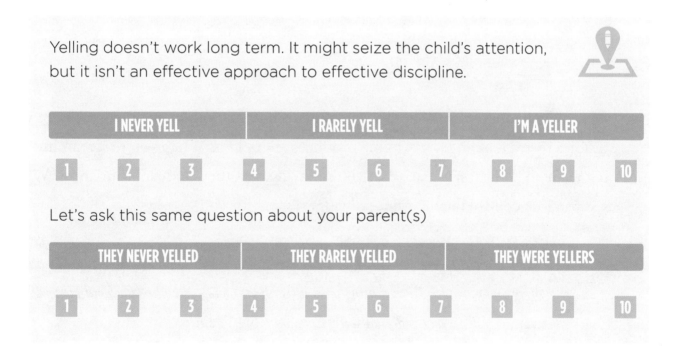

Yelling doesn't work long term. It might seize the child's attention, but it isn't an effective approach to effective discipline.

I NEVER YELL			I RARELY YELL			I'M A YELLER		
1	2	3	4	5	6	7	8	9	10

Let's ask this same question about your parent(s)

THEY NEVER YELLED			THEY RARELY YELLED			THEY WERE YELLERS		
1	2	3	4	5	6	7	8	9	10

So much of our parenting script is picked up from how we were parented. Even if you said, "I never want to act like my parents…" there's a good chance you do or will unless you take intentional steps to break away from the habits you learned and rewrite your parenting script.

Yellers tend to come from homes where yelling was modeled. If you are currently on[e] who yells, please take some time to stop and think about the impact of your yelling. You'[ll] probably come to the conclusion that yelling isn't working anyway. There are more effec[c-] tive ways to communicate that won't wound, scare, and shame your children.

Circle the word below that most closely applies to your go-to response in a discipline situation:

Ignore	Excuse	Quick-fix/Yell
Angry/Over-discipline	Thought-through	Downplay
Yell/Spank	Extreme Consequences	Intentional
Send to room	Other: (describe)	

Discipline in anger results in embarrassment, humiliation, and sometimes even violence[.] Studies reveal that angry discipline produces angry kids. When you're screaming and yell[l-] ing at them, kids don't hear what you're saying, but they do hear your spirit. When the[y] see you lose control they'll eventually lose respect for you.

"Now a word to you parents. Don't keep on scolding and nagging your children, making the[m] angry and resentful. Rather, bring them up with the loving discipline the Lord Himself approve[s] with suggestions and godly advice." Ephesians 6:4 (TLB)

WHEN YOU'RE SCREAMING AND YELLING AT THEM, **KIDS DON'T HEAR WHAT YOU'RE SAYING,** BUT THEY DO HEAR YOUR SPIRIT.

DISCIPLINE WITH CAUTION

Bodies are fragile, but spirits are even more fragile. No loving parent wants their children to live in fear of anger.

How often are you physical with your discipline? Being physical refers to spanking, slapping, grabbing, squeezing — essentially anything that attempts to threaten with force.

We are not making a statement about spanking or not spanking here — we tried both approaches with our children. We are suggesting that, in whatever you decide, you deal with your own anger before you discipline so you can be delicate and thoughtful.

You've learned by now that we believe being an Intentional Parent is not only more difficult, it's also more time consuming. A quick-fix is to simply yell and spank when anger arises. Problem solved. Right? As the child runs to his room crying, we think the behavior has been fixed… or, at least we feel better for the moment.

When we don't take time to cool off and address our anger, we tend to do and say things that are not only dumb, but also damaging.

Intentional Parents know how each of their children typically "pushes their buttons," and so they plan for this and make pre-decisions on how they will handle each situation.

These situations are going to happen again. When they do, what will you do to minimize your anger? Make those decisions ahead of time so you'll be ready when you children begin pushing your buttons again.

ACTIVITY:
DISCIPLINE WITH CAUTION

List each of your children below and write a word or two describing what they normally do that annoys you and triggers your anger. Try to keep this limited to one or two actions.

NAME	ACTION THAT IGNITES MY ANGER	HOW MIGHT I MINIMIZE MY DISPLAY OF ANGER

Will implementing this be difficult for you? Why or why not?

_____

_____

_____

An Intentional Parent, regardless of the situation, makes the pre-decision to:

- Stay calm
- Work to be wise with discipline
- Enforce consequences regardless of the child's response.

As a parent, you are in control. You don't have to always provide discipline immediately. You're not a police officer who is mandated to give out violations as soon as the infraction is identified. You can choose to take time to cool off to prevent you from disciplining in anger.

◈ DISCIPLINE BY CHOICE

When your children are old enough to reason, we believe the best discipline is what we call "discipline by choice." When you employ discipline by choice, you don't have to get mad, impulsively punish, or spontaneously spank.

Discipline by choice includes: (1) a fair consequence that is (2) clearly communicated ahead of time, and (3) connected to the offense.

Let's look more closely at these: **A fair consequence** is reasonable — this means it's not too harsh and not too light. It's a measured, logical consequence. It also means it's respectful — the goal of a consequence isn't to get revenge, it's to help the child better understand the connection between choices and results.

Clearly communicating ahead of time means that you don't surprise your child with consequences that you make up in the momentary impulse of your anger. Rather, in age-appropriate language, you can calmly and clearly say,

> *"If you choose to [fill-in-the-blank], then I want to be real clear that your choice will result in [fill-in-the-consequence]."*

Clear. Simple. Understandable. Done. Please don't miss this: when this approach is in play, the consequence ultimately becomes the child's choice. This helps teach the connection between choices and consequences.

Connected to the offense means that (when possible) connect the consequence to the behavior in question. If your child is trying to run over the cat on his tricycle, don't take away the TV for a month; restrict time with the tricycle.

When discipline by choice is done right, it doesn't have to set you up against your children.

QUICK-FIX DISCIPLINE

PARENT VS. CHILD

INTENTIONAL DISCIPLINE

PARENT / CHILD VS. CONSEQUENCE

When you have an agreed upon consequence — that neither parent nor child wants to see happen — you are not adversaries with your child. You can graciously remind her about the consequence without threatening, posturing, manipulating, or shaming. Encourage her to make the right decision, but we don't make the decision for her.

If she doesn't make the right decision, your role is to enforce the consequence.

In our family, if one of our children violated curfew, we could calmly and confidently say, "I'm glad you're home safely. I hope you had fun tonight. I was getting a little worried, but then I began to feel sad for you. I was beginning to think about what a drag it will be for you to be home with your mom and me for the next three weekends. I was feeling awful, but I figured you took all that into consideration when you made the choice to be late. I'm not sure if you think it was a good or bad choice, but all choices have consequences."

Most likely your child will get mad and upset when you enforce consequences. No matter how clear and kind you are, he won't say: *"Thank you for being such a wise, caring, and Intentional Parent. I'm honored that you're my dad."* That won't happen… at least it never did with us. The only one he will legitimately have to be mad at is himself, because he was in total control of the outcome.

When you discipline this way, it relieves you from having to act like a fool and yell and scream and posture and threaten and shame.

The most difficult part of all of this is actually enforcing the consequence. If you can't enforce discipline by choice, you'll struggle being an Intentional (and effective) Parent. In addition, your child will never develop the much-needed character quality of responsibility (which we'll discuss in the next chapter).

ACTIVITY:
DISCIPLINE BY CHOICE

What is your gut reaction to reading about "discipline by choice"?

_____

_____

What do you envision to be some difficulties for you with this parenting/discipline approach?

_____

_____

What are the benefits you can see with discipline by choice?

_____

_____

Is enforcing consequences difficult for you? Why or why not?

_____

_____

What are some situations you've experienced where the consequence become inconvenient for you?

_____

_____

To stop what you are doing in order to take your child aside definitely requires energy and self-control. How good are you at this on a scale of 1-10?

1 = I NEVER DO THIS—I YELL FROM WHEREVER I AM	10 = I AM SO PATIENT—MY CHILD COULD RECITE THE GETTYSBURG ADDRESS WHILE WAITING FOR ME TO MOVE INTO ACTION

| 1 | 2 | 3 | 4 | 5 | 6 | 7 | 8 | 9 | 10 |

What do you think is the outcome of a child who doesn't experience consequences?

_____

_____

"A prudent person foresees the danger ahead and takes precautions. The simpleton goes blindly on and suffers the consequences." Proverbs 27:12 (NLT)

When we don't allow our children to experience fair and natural consequences, they will remain a simpleton, and their ability to develop a mature sense of decision-making and responsibility will be stunted.

 Here is an example of questions we tried to ask during moments of discipline:

1. [calmly] **"What did you do?"**

2. **"Was that right or wrong?"** This question gets them thinking about the value of *character*.

3. **"How could you have handled this better?"** Now, we're moving toward developing *competence*.

4. **"Next time, what do you think you should do?** In some situations, this will ignite conversations on *compassion*.

5. **"Should you choose the wrong action, what might be a fair and natural consequence?"** As the parent you have the final call on what the consequences will be, but when you allow children to weigh in on establishing consequences, the chances are better that they will support what they helped create. There were many occasions when our children created more severe consequences than we were even contemplating.

Parenting requires energy! Discipline is one of the most exhausting dimensions of being a parent. Give yourself time, and also give yourself a break. Think through ways to be more effective so you don't have to be a Quick-Fix Parent and act on your impulses.

TAKE ACTION

What needs to be improved in your discipline style and actions? How will you attempt to improve?

_____

_____

_____

_____

If married, are you and your spouse normally on the same page in regard to discipline? If not, what steps can you take to come to an agreement?

_____

_____

_____

_____

If you and your spouse don't share the same discipline style, you must take time together to discuss the essential actions for effective discipline. This is the required work of Intentional Parents. Talk about the specific actions that will work for both of you while guiding your children with love.

Please watch the "Delicate Discipline & Activate Responsibility" Discussion Video with Doug & Cathy.

ACTION 8
ACTIVATE RESPONSIBILITY

ACTION 8 ACTIVATE RESPONSIBILITY

Intentional Parents provide opportunities for their children to develop responsibility and pursue healthy independence.

If you have not already done so, watch the "Delicate Discipline & Activate Responsibility" Teaching Video prior to reading this chapter.

When people find out that we're advocates for kids or that we speak on parent/child relationships, eventually this question arises, *"Why are today's kids so irresponsible?"*

You don't have to look too far to see examples for why this is a valid question. It's displayed daily by millions of children who reflect this in what we call the ABC's of irresponsibility:

Apathy: "I don't care about being responsible."

Blame: "It's not my fault." This is where the other person is always wrong. The dumb teacher. The stupid coach. My lame parents.

Care-for-me mentality: "I've been cradled my entire life. Somebody else will figure it out or do it for me and save me from the consequences."

Our answer to the *"why are today's kids so irresponsible"* question is: Responsibility is not genetic. Children are not born with a sense of responsibility. They must be taught to develop it by being given significant opportunities to practice.

Let's consider a few examples of how we might be contributing to our children's irresponsibility:

1. **BY ALWAYS PICKING UP AFTER THEM AND NOT MAKING THEM CONTRIBUTE.**

   - *"I know you'll never clean this up, so I might as well do it myself."*

2. **BY MAKING MONEY TOO EASILY AVAILABLE AND NOT VALUABLE ENOUGH.**

   - *"This is the last time I pay for this. Next time you're going to have to earn this."*

3. **BY TELLING THEM THEY CAN DO NO WRONG.**

   - *"It's not your fault that you got a low grade, sweetheart — your teacher is just inexperienced."*

4. **By solving all their problems and saving them from experiencing consequences.**

   - *"Don't worry, I'll make sure to tell the coach that you forgot your cleats so you don't get in trouble."*

RESPONSIBILITY IS NOT GENETIC.

ACTIVITY:
ACTIVATE RESPONSIBILITY

When you read those examples, was there any part of you that thought, "Hmmm... that might be me"? If so, which one? Why do you think you do that?

_____

_____

_____

What are other ways you have observed parents contributing to the irresponsibility of their children?

_____

_____

_____

The goal behind trying to activate responsibility within children is to guide them to move from infantile dependence to healthy independence.

Let's think about your own children — if 1 represents infantile dependence and 10 is healthy independence, evaluate where you'd place each of your children.

INFANTILE DEPENDENCE					HEALTHY INDEPENDENCE				
1	2	3	4	5	6	7	8	9	10

Name: _____

Name: _____

Name: _____

Name: _____

ACTIVITY:
DISCIPLINE BY CHOICE (CONT'D)

What are you currently doing with each of your children to allow them to experience some "real" responsibility within your family?

NAME	AGE	RESPONSIBILITY

Look over your answers and ask yourself, "Is the responsibility age-appropriate for each child? Or, is it too easy/difficult for their current ages?"

_____

_____

_____

_____

◈ ACTIVATE RESPONSIBILITY

One of the primary purposes of chores is to teach responsibility. Chores help children learn important life skills while promoting responsible behavior.

In our grandparents' era, if the children didn't pull their weight and help out on the family farm, there were natural consequences — they wouldn't eat. Those daily chores contributed to the family while giving the children meaning, value, and opportunities to develop into capable, self-reliant adults.

In today's urban, suburban, technological society, many children have never had the opportunity to accept any real meaningful responsibility. Everything is easy. It's done for them or contracted out to others.

Today, we don't need our children to help us put food on the table. If we're honest, children actually complicate our lives and get in the way of us being more productive (maybe that's why the government refers to them as a "deduction"). They're a wonderful complication, but since we don't need them to milk the cows and gather the eggs, they can miss out on opportunities to develop a work ethic that's connected to responsibility.

Sadly, we've observed some of our kids' friends who couldn't wake themselves up in the morning (for a sports' practice or school) because they had never been given the responsibility of doing it themselves. Their parents did it for them. So when they would spend the night at our house, they were actually surprised when we weren't their human alarm clocks.

Intentional Parents think through and assign age-appropriate chores that are connected to service and responsibility. In addition, these chores are linked with consequences in case the child chooses irresponsibility.

Chores are not punishment; they're part of growing up in a healthy home where everyone contributes and plays a role. Regardless of economic ability, parents shouldn't outsource child-friendly chores.

What are you currently doing that you could assign as a chore to a child? Make a list below:

_____

_____

_____

_____

We're intentionally choosing to be very general in what we communicate here about chores. We don't have the specific answers for your family to questions such as: How many chores? How often? How long? Those are questions for you to answer as you think through your kids' ages and their current schedules. We lived with the principle that as long as you're living at home, you contribute. You don't graduate from family responsibility until you leave the home.

During our kids' busier seasons, we would back down on some of the chore expectations. We viewed their participation on different sports teams as one avenue that helped them develop responsibility. Playing on a team or being involved in an activity outside of school came with its own responsibilities and consequences.

For example, if we drove our child to a soccer game and she forgot her cleats, the consequence was that she didn't play for that one game. Our reasoning was that if we raced home to save her by getting her cleats, chances were good that she'd allow that to happen again. With the consequence of missing a game she loves to play, she became more responsible to pack her own bag.

When parents are quick to bail their kids out each time they fail, they quench an opportunity to build responsibility.

At our seminars we often bring up the familiar "forgotten lunch scenario" and ask parents to raise their hands if they take the lunch to school when they realize their child left it at home. There's usually an awkward laugh before hands start popping up. When we ask the simple question, "Why?" there will always be one parent who says, "I only do it because I don't want her to starve to death."

We don't want your child to starve either. That would be terrible. But, did you know it takes the average person over 60 days with no food before they'll die of starvation? This means your kids will be able to survive a few hours without food, and when they return home hungry, they will also learn that getting their lunch to school was their responsibility… not yours.

"I don't want her to starve to death."

Do you agree or disagree with our forgotten lunch illustration? Why?

_____

_____

What are some examples of where you (or your spouse) might be currently preventing your children from experiencing consequences?

_____

_____

_____

Responsibility begins to be formed when children are young and parents follow through with clear consequences connected to clear tasks. If not, boundaries become meaningless

A perfect example of this is, "How many times do I have to tell you…?" We found that if we asked our kids to do something and they always replied with, "I will, I'll do it later"… well, they never did or they "forgot." We had to make them stop and do it right then, or make a note of it and make sure it was done before bedtime. They knew that was the deal. Because of this, they were not surprised if we went into their room as they were getting ready for bed (or in bed) and told them it needed to be done. They learned quickly it was best to do the job *now*.

This is the primary way young people learn how to become responsible. A child's ability to make decisions and avoid consequences can build self-esteem. When a child learns that behaviors have consequences, he will learn that he has power and control over his own life.

> "I'm in control."
> "I'm not a victim."
> "I have power over consequences."

These are very positive, important lessons for a child to learn, and the great news is that it's not too late to begin any of this.

A CHILD'S ABILITY TO MAKE DECISIONS AND AVOID CONSEQUENCES CAN BUILD SELF-ESTEEM.

TAKE ACTION

Make a list of age-appropriate responsibilities and chores or everyday actions you can use to help develop your children's responsibility.

NAME	AGE	CHORE/RESPONSIBILITY

How do you envision your child struggling with these responsibilities? What can you do to empower responsibility without taking the chores back and doing it yourself?

NAME	AGE	HAS HARD TIME	HOW CAN I HELP

If you have not already done so, please watch the "Delicate Discipline & Activate Responsibility" Discussion Video with Doug & Cathy.

ACTION 9
POSITIVE MEMORIES

ACTION 9 POSITIVE MEMORIES

Intentional Parents pursue opportunities to become memory makers.

Watch the "Positive Memories & Serious Fun" Teaching Video prior to reading this chapter.

Our goal throughout this workbook is to make it clear that there is no such thing as a perfect parent. Since that's true, we could also reason there is no such thing as a perfect family.

We want you to keep that in mind as you think more deeply about being a memory-making parent. For some reason, this idea of being an intentional memory maker seems to trigger a lot of parental guilt. You don't need more guilt. Relax.

Let's agree that every parent is going to create some bad memories for their children. That includes us, and it includes you too. You're going to make mistakes. You're going to say terrible words. You're going to display childish behavior that is unbecoming of an adult. You're going to get angry, and it's going to be ugly. This is going to happen during your child's 18 years … 6,570 days … 936 weeks … 216 months.

How beautiful will it be, though, if the positive memories far outweigh the negative? That's a great goal to set for yourself as an Intentional Parent.

Dream about the future for a moment. Imagine your adult children reflecting on their childhoods and experiencing a flood of positive memories. When that time comes, they will be so grateful that you chose the goal to make good memories outweigh the bad.

OUR OWN CHILDHOOD MEMORIES ARE STRONG AND VIVID

- [Cathy] Learning to ride my bike and my dad clapping with a big smile.

- [Doug] My mom being at all my games and cheering for me (even when I sat on the bench).

- [Cathy] My mom welcoming all my friends to our house and always having great snacks.

- [Doug] Summer driving vacations and only staying in motels with pools. Driving through Mississippi where I naively asked, "Where's Mr. Sippi?" My parents laughed, then the dog barked and I gave him a LifeSaver; he then choked and threw up on my sister. So much fun.

Memories seem to be important to God too. A brief scan of the Bible reveals that God established several memory builders.

- Sabbath: a day set aside each week to *remember* God as creator.

- Feasts: to *remember* that God is both holy and our provider.

- Communion: to *remember* what Jesus did on the cross as payment for our sins.

- Memorials/altars: to *remember* specific places where God did great things.

God seems to want us to remember that which is good about Him and His character and to pass that on. Spiritual memories are significant.

> *"Only be careful, and watch yourselves closely so that you do not forget the things your eyes have seen or let them fade from your heart as long as you live. Teach them to your children and to their children after them." Deuteronomy 4:9 (NIV)*

ACTIVITY:
POSITIVE MEMORIES

Before we get into creating family memories, let's consider passing on spiritual memories.

Have you told your children about your own spiritual story? Do they know your testimony? If not, take some time here to write down some of the key elements that would help you share that very important story.

_____

_____

_____

What are some spiritual traditions you plan to pass on to your children?

_____

_____

_____

Think about it like this: Our lives are a museum of memories that contribute to who we are and who we become. Every memory is like a frame in a film of life, and each frame adds to our identity and health as human beings.

Write five of your favorite memories that you have with your parent(s).

1. _____

2. _____

3. _____

4. _____

5. _____

How do you think those positive memories helped shape who you are today?

_____

_____

_____

We realize that many parents come from homes where all that is remembered is pain, abuse, and negative situations. The picture of the growing-up years isn't bright in those cases. If that describes you, we are so sorry, and we don't pretend to understand the depth of your pain. What we do know is that you want a different, brighter future for your children. You know all too well the power of memories, and we believe you can redeem your painful memories by creating great ones for your kids.

Memories build on the foundation of who we are.

As a parent, building memories for your child is not a choice. The question is — what kind of memories will they be? Good ones? Bad ones? When the frames of experience are all spliced together in the movie of your life, what story will they tell?

- A mom who was a nag…or a mom who was playful?
- A dad who was rarely present…or a dad who was present and passionate?
- Parents who always said "no"…or parents who were liberal with their "yes's" and selective with their "no's"?
- Parents who acted like roommates…or parents who were crazy about each other?
- Parents who yelled all the time…or parents who laughed a lot?

IMAGINE YOUR ADULT CHILDREN REFLECTING ON THEIR CHILDHOODS AND EXPERIENCING **A FLOOD OF POSITIVE MEMORIES.**

ACTIVITY:
POSITIVE MEMORIES

If nothing changed about your current home or your parenting, what do you think your child's primary memories would be?

_____

_____

What might be some easy ways for you to create and capture memories? Take time to write down some ideas that could contribute to making memories next to each of the following headings:

Surprise:

_____

_____

Photos:

_____

_____

Laughter:

_____

_____

Trips/vacations:

_____

_____

Family meals:

_____

_____

Special events:

_____

_____

Other:

_____

_____

HERE ARE SOME OF OUR IDEAS TO BECOME MORE EFFECTIVE AT MAKING MEMORIES:

Family vacations: research reveals that vacations typically provide children with the strongest family memories.

We discovered early in our marriage that there was never a good time to take a vacation. We had great memories of vacations from our own childhoods, and we really wanted this for our kids too. It took us a few years to figure out that we just had to get it on the calendar and go. There would always be hurdles and excuses as we neared the date, but if specific dates were blocked out on the calendar, it was a done deal. The times vacations didn't happen were when we had said, "We should get away some time in the spring." Vague doesn't work. It won't become dynamic until it becomes specific. Get it on the calendar. Money and time are not strong enough excuses — it doesn't have to be an expensive vacation to create great memories.

Ideas and potential dates for your next family vacation:

_____

_____

_____

Spontaneous adventures: these are the memories we created that were less vacation and more like special events. For example, during the kids' spring break we'd go to work in orphanages in Mexico with the church's youth group. A couple Sunday nights every year we'd take jackets and blankets into the inner city of Los Angeles for the homeless. When one of our kids' soccer or baseball games was rained out, we would turn it into an opportunity to do something else fun. The time was already blocked out anyway, so why let rain stop us?

These little adventures didn't require a lot of money or planning (hence, "spontaneous"). We decided that our kids would rather be in an old, clunky car headed toward an adventure than have a nice Mercedes parked in the driveway (or at the office).

Ideas and potential dates for the next spontaneous adventure:

_____

_____

_____

Made-up traditions: these were the memories we created on-the-go. They were both simple and silly. Every Monday was our family date night. The tradition was that each family member got a turn to choose how we would spend Monday dinner, plus two hours. It might be as simple as McDonalds and batting cages (our son) or as weird as eating spaghetti with chopsticks on our trampoline (Doug). The fun part was that each person (yes, as parents we took a turn too) had a month to think about their next Monday date night option. Other made-up traditions included: Christmas Eve, Christmas Day, last day of school, last day of summer, Survivor Finale TV block party, birthdays, etc.

What are some of the traditions in your home? The ones that when your kids are older they will look back on and say, "Every birthday we would…" or, "Every Sunday night we did this…" Write out a few traditions that are currently happening in your home:

Ideas for more made-up traditions:

_____

_____

_____

Capture memories: in our digital age, there's really no excuse to not capture, document, and replay memories. The beauty of every photo is that it has a story behind it. As children grow older the good stories are retold as they develop new friends who enter your home and see the memories in photo books or hanging on the walls.

From the time they were little, we told our children they could save their money instead of buying presents for us on our birthdays and Christmas; the only gifts we wanted were photos, and as they got older, accompanying letters. We often laugh now because we have so many photos and videos, it would take years to consume them.

Today, the subject of photos and videos always comes up around the holidays when our adult children return home and watch family videos, laugh, and retell stories. We're able to sit back and enjoy our children enjoying parts of their childhood that we captured. Photos and videos are such a beautiful gift to the family memory.

Write letters, cards, and notes: at some point your child may begin to wonder, "Does anyone really care about me? Does anyone know I'm alive? Does anyone really love me?" Imagine if they had a box full of letters, and during those dark moments that box screamed, "Look over here! Look at all these letters, cards and notes your parents have given you over the years. I know you're discouraged right now, but read these and see that you are deeply loved."

Regularly writing letters, cards, and small index card-sized notes to your children will serve as reminders of your love to them. Your words matter deeply — especially when you express love through them.

Building memories will earn you an A in parenting, and it's never too late to start!

We both have lost parents and loved ones and have spent a lot of time with them during their last days. The dying don't ask to be surrounded by their trophies or to see a pie chart of their 401K retirement accounts. They want to be around family, they want to look at photos, recall stories, and think about all the good memories — that is what sums up life.

Memories matter…good parents are intentional about making them happen.

TAKE ACTION

How will you begin planning some family memories? Be proactive here. Can you think of any ideas you can do this week that will make memories? Think of something "small" that you can do everyday this week to get you in the memory making habit.

Here are some ideas to get you started:

- Home-made movie Monday.
- Taco Tuesday tradition.
- Wear-whatever-you-want-Wednesday.
- Trick-or-Treat Thursday (a candy-raid at the nearest store)
- Fun Friday — everyone takes a turn coming up with something to do.

Now, it's your turn… what are some options for Saturday or Sunday that don't include Sleeping-in-Saturday, or Leave-me-alone-Sunday?

_____

_____

_____

Write a note to each of your children this week (a love note, a fun note, a phrase of affirmation, a blessing, etc.).

Take a photo of something that happens this week during your memory making attempt. Print it out, hang it up, and memorialize that specific memory.

Please watch the "Positive Memories & Serious Fun" Discussion Video with Doug & Cathy.

ACTION 10

SERIOUS FUN

ACTION 10 SERIOUS FUN

Intentional Parents nurture laughter and fun.

 If you have not already done so, watch the "Positive Memories & Serious Fun" Teaching Video prior to reading this chapter.

Congratulations, you're almost done — only one more chapter to work through! We are fully aware that you may have read this chapter title and considered skipping it. Did you think, *"Fun? Really? That makes the top-ten list of essential actions all parents need to take?"*

Absolutely! We've added the modifier "serious" to the chapter heading to emphasize its importance. We believe this chapter is worthy of some of your very best consideration, and we want you to become serious about fun and laughter within your family.

Currently, how important is fun and laughter in your family?
Do you see any value in it for families?

_____

_____

"Fun" may seem like a shallow idea, but it has the power to change the way your children grow up. Why? Because today's generation lives in a faster paced, more radically changing society than you experienced growing up. Children feel enormous pressure from driven parents to perform and succeed. A lot of this pressure is motivated by parents who want to feel better about themselves, and they use their children to do so. It's sad to find parents who make their parenting decisions to enhance their own identities.

ACTIVITY:
SERIOUS FUN

How much thought have you given to the importance of fun in your home?

NONE									I'VE CONSIDERED IT A LOT!
1	2	3	4	5	6	7	8	9	10

Can you think of any areas you're adding pressure to your children so that you can "look better" or "feel better" about yourself? If so, what areas? Why do you think you do this?

_____

_____

If you are not trying to enhance your identity through your parenting, can you see examples of other parents who are? Where do you see it happening? Or, if you're a new parent, in what situations can you imagine this type of pressure happening?

_____

_____

If your children are young, what pressures do you envision them facing in the next decade? If your children are pre-teens or teenagers, what pressures do you know they're currently experiencing?

_____

What about you and your own personal, fun quotient? Check the box that best describes your personality:

- ☐ I make Scrooge look fun.
- ☐ I've laughed a couple of times this year.
- ☐ I've laughed more than a couple of times this year, but I'm not sure how often.
- ☐ I know fun is important, but I'm not sure how to make it happen.
- ☐ I'm not the most fun person ever, but I enjoy having a good time.
- ☐ I'm not boring, but I'm not the life of the party.
- ☐ I really appreciate and value fun for my family, but it doesn't describe me.
- ☐ Laughter and fun is definitely very important to me.
- ☐ I am the life of the party—I leak fun everywhere I go.
- ☐ Comedians and late-night television hosts seek me out for material.

ACTIVITY:
SERIOUS FUN (CONT'D)

What are you currently doing to ensure there's fun happening within your home?

_____

_____

What makes the idea of fun difficult for you?

_____

_____

This specific Biblical Proverb tells us that a joyful heart is good for us both physically and emotionally.

> "A cheerful heart is good medicine, but a broken spirit saps a person's strength."
> Proverbs 17:22 (NLT)

How do you think fun could act as good medicine for your children?

_____

_____

_____

Let's consider some specific ways fun and laughter can impact a young person's life. Rank these results in order of most to least importance to you:

1 = least important; 4 = most important.

____ It helps them release anxieties.

____ It helps them diminish fears.

____ It lessens hostility.

____ It reduces built-up anger.

Where we live in southern California there was recently a car full of teenagers who drove by innocent people and shot them with a paintball gun. The paintballs splattered on the victims with such force that they assumed they were being blasted by a real gun. The teenagers in the car videotaped the victims' reactions during this dangerous prank, and after their arrest the video went viral. Major news outlets picked up the story, reporters interviewed victims, commentators pontificated on the evils of gang life, and it became exhibit A on the condition of today's tragic teenager.

Here's what we found interesting about the entire event: childlike laughter filled the teens' car as they fired their paintballs. It was undeniable, genuine, innocent-sounding laughter. These were hardened gang kids — some with criminal records — who were giggling like schoolgirls.

While there's no way we condone their actions, we did find the passion of their laughter revealing. Every kid needs to laugh and play and have fun…even the most misguided of them. Kids must experience fun to be fully healthy and alive.

Have you ever heard the phrase, "laughter is the best medicine"? Well it turns out that it may be more scientific than we ever knew.

An article on the Science Daily website discusses the connection between laughter and health.

"… the best clinicians understand that there is an intrinsic physiological intervention brought about by positive emotions such as mirthful laughter, optimism and hope. Lifestyle choices have a significant impact on health and disease…"[5]

5. American Physiological Society. "Laughter Remains Good Medicine." ScienceDaily. ScienceDaily, 17 April 2009.

We believe parents can lead the way and model fun for children. Don't worry, you don't need to become a stand-up comedian to be a great parent, but you do need to know how to find fun and develop it in your home.

How are you currently modeling fun for your kids? If you're not, how might you begin?

_____

_____

_____

We've made it no secret throughout this workbook that we are both followers of Jesus. We have been since our teenage years. We've also spent more than thirty years recruiting adults to hang out with teenagers and disciple them in the ways of Jesus. One principle we have learned to be true is that adults who are fun, or at least open to having fun, are the ones who are able to best connect with teenagers. Here's what's counterintuitive: this attraction doesn't have anything to do with age, economics, having a better grasp on teen culture, or possessing a "coolness" factor. Adults who have the ability to draw kids in, communicate with them, invest in their lives, and mentor them are the ones with playful spirits.

We believe those of us who have aligned our lives with Jesus ought to be leading the way in modeling fun. Unfortunately, this isn't a universally shared belief. We have come across many Christians who believe that the more serious you are the more spiritually mature you are. Children would say that the more serious you are... the more boring you are!

LIGHTEN UP

If you read the book of Ecclesiastes, you'll learn that one of the necessary rhythms of life is laughter and dance.

> *"For everything there is a season,*
> *a time for every activity under heaven.*
>
> *a time to cry and a time to laugh.*
> *A time to grieve and a time to dance." (3:1,4) (NLT)*

If you want to fully live and understand what it means to live abundantly, meaningfully, and joyfully, you've got to dance and laugh — it's one of the necessary rhythms of life.

I [Doug] am thankful God gave us laughter and dance because I'd rather die than dance — it's not a pretty site. At weddings, when I'm dancing, someone usually calls the paramedics when they see me.

We're confident that Jesus laughed. We don't have Biblical proof that he sat around the campfire and cracked jokes, but since Biblical teaching tells us that Jesus was one hundred percent God while at the same time one hundred percent human — this is easy to imagine. Humans laugh, and Jesus was surrounded by plenty of material to feed that laughter.

Consider how he encountered life — Jesus spent a lot of time walking and camping with twelve young men! You know there had to be a few "pull-my-finger" moments. At least once Peter had to say something funny that caused Jesus to laugh so hard that he snorted. Who knows? Maybe Andrew said, *"Was that a snort? Hey you guys — Jesus snorted."*

Do you have a hard time thinking that way about Jesus? Are you wired or conditioned to believe, "No way! Jesus didn't do that. He might have said, *'Thou art funny Peter! I delighteth in your jesting! You maketh me snorteth goat's milk outeth thine nasal passageth.'* "

If you believe that Jesus never laughed, never smiled, never used humor, or enjoyed having fun, then you may have a totally underdeveloped view of who God is. That limited view of God can shape how you live your life. When you have a picture in your mind of a stern, scowling, always-mad God it can make it difficult to approach God in prayer.

What do you think? Do you believe God values laughter and fun? Why or why not?

_____

_____

OXYMORON: SCHEDULED FUN

Your kids may need you to lighten up. They need you to relax. Smile. Play. Laugh. Enjoy life. And schedule some family fun. We realize "scheduling fun" may seem like an oxymoron (two words that don't go together: i.e. free trade, death benefits, pretty ugly, etc…), but that may be exactly what's needed for fun to make an appearance in your home.

One thing we started doing spontaneously for fun in our family was rainy day slip-and-slide. In southern California rainy days didn't happen all that often, but when they did, we loved to go outside and play. One time we discovered the idea of dressing in large trash bags, squirting each other with dish soap, then running and sliding in the yard. It might have been a little dangerous, but most of the time when we did things like this, it was one of us parents who got hurt. If someone breaks an arm, it adds to the memory making (remember the last chapter?)!

What are a couple ideas of scheduled fun that pop into your mind?

_____

_____

Here's the deal: if kids don't get fun at home, we promise you… they will try to find it somewhere else, and it may not be the kind of fun you had in mind. Think drive-by paint-ball shootings.

We are totally convinced that one of the reasons our older children (all in their 20's) still like to come back and be around our house (besides free food and laundry) is because we have worked very hard to make our home a place where fun is valued. For example:

"FUN AND HAPPINESS IS CONTAGIOUS."

- Humorous movies and TV shows are our go-to genre.
- Humor is valued and encouraged.
- We take pleasure in scaring one another throughout the house.
- We don't take ourselves too seriously.
- We appreciate hearing a good, humorous story.
- Most of our family photos include at least one of us "ruining it" by making a funny face.
- We pride ourselves on making others in the family laugh.

Fun and happiness are contagious. Laughter not only heals our body, it improves one's outlook on life. When our kids were little we heard a child psychologist say something like, "It's better for you to encourage your child to watch a funny YouTube video before a big test than to pester him/her with questions about being ready, relaxed, and focused. The best thing you can do for them is send them out the door with a smile on their face and laughter in their heart. They'll perform much better."

We can't remember the psychologist's name, but when we heard her say that, we listened and both thought, "We can do that! We will do that!"

Are you okay with laughing at yourself? Make it safe for your kids to laugh at you. What will you need to do to lighten up and laugh at yourself?

Smile more. Laugh at the little things. Don't waste your time trying to defend yourself. Stop getting mad when your kids point out something that you did that was funny to them. Who cares? They love you — they actually think you're secure enough to allow them to laugh at you. Laugh with them. Nurture their laughter. Let them see that there are a few things in life that you take very seriously: your relationship with Jesus, your marriage, and your desire to be an Intentional Parent. But for most other things, chill, relax, enjoy the moment, and laugh it off.

One last thought about fun in your family: Fun doesn't have to be what's fun for you. So what if it's not fun for you? Do it anyway. Intentional Parents are sacrificial parents. If it's fun for your child, go along with it and just remember that you've only got 216 months or less to enjoy what they're enjoying.

TAKE ACTION

Let's schedule some fun right now. What is one action you can take to be more fun?

Today _____

This week _____

This month _____

What's a long-term fun plan for your family?

_____

_____

Now, let's get even more specific. Put a fun activity next to each child:

NAME	FUN ACTIVITY

If you have not already done so, please watch the "Positive Memories & Serious Fun" Discussion Video with Doug & Cathy.

◈ A FINAL WORD

Congratulations on finishing this series. Way to go! We don't take what you just accomplished lightly. It's a huge deal. You have taken a big step to become a more effective parent. You are parenting in a culture that relies on quick-fix answers rather than reading and reflecting and answering tough questions like you just did. Again, congratulations for your effort.

Our hope and prayer is that you've learned some things that you can apply to your parenting that will not only make your life easier, but will make your child's life better. Remember, it's a journey… a long one. Keep taking intentional steps. Don't try to master all 10 of these actions at once. Focus on a couple of them and then return to the others. You and your parenting are a work in progress.

Honored to be with you in a small part of your journey,

- Doug & Cathy

◈ ABOUT THE AUTHORS

Doug & Cathy Fields have been married over 30 years and have 3 grown children in their 20's. Their primary passion and joy have been family, but along the way they spent their years helping others — especially young people. They have worked at both Mariners and Saddleback Church in Southern California for 3 decades as youth, family, and teaching pastors. Doug is an author (60+ books), consultant, co-founder of Downloadyouthministry.com, and he is the Director of HomeWord's Center for Youth & Family at Azusa Pacific University. Cathy and Doug speak together on marriage and parenting and have more information available at www.DougFields.com.

INTENTIONAL PARENTING

BY DOUG & CATHY FIELDS

ACTION 1: STRONG BELIEF

Intentional Parents believe they have incredible influence on their children.

ACTION 2: 24/7 ROLE MODEL

Intentional Parents understand that children learn from observing them as their primary role models.

ACTION 3: ENCOURAGING WORDS

Intentional Parents regularly use words that are positive and life-giving.

ACTION 4: GENUINE AFFECTION

Intentional Parents liberally give affection.

ACTION 5: CONSISTENT PRESENCE

Intentional Parents make sacrifices in order to be consistently present.

ACTION 6: PEACEFUL HOME

Intentional Parents create a shelter from the storm.

ACTION 7: DELICATE DISCIPLINE

Intentional Parents view discipline as guidance with love.

ACTION 8: ACTIVATE RESPONSIBILITY

Intentional Parents provide opportunities for their children to develop responsibility and pursue healthy independence.

ACTION 9: POSITIVE MEMORIES

Intentional Parents pursue opportunities to become memory makers.

ACTION 10: SERIOUS FUN

Intentional Parents nurture laughter and fun.

GROUP
DISCUSSION GUIDE

TABLE OF CONTENTS

LEADING FOR THE FIRST TIME

Thank you for facilitating a discussion about how to be an effective parent! We've given you tips here about how to guide a conversation with a group of people.

WHAT YOU'LL NEED

- Videos for your group, either via Streaming Online (included) or DVD (sold separately)
- Workbooks for each participant in your group (we recommend one per person, or one spouse will tend to do everything at the exclusion of the other)
- This Group Discussion Guide

HOW TO USE THIS DISCUSSION GUIDE

Below you'll see a breakdown of each session and how to navigate the Videos and Workbook. Before you get started, we recommend you review all of the material each week in advance (Videos, Workbook and Discussion Guide). You'll notice common elements in this discussion guide: (1) START, (2) WATCH VIDEO ONE, (3) WATCH VIDEO TWO, (4) DISCUSSION, and (5) DO. Here's some basic information about how they all flow together.

START (15 MINUTES)

This is a simple, but important icebreaker to use before you watch the video. It's a "teaser" of sorts to get people focused on the weekly subject. These icebreakers are meant to be easy ones that anyone can answer. Essentially, it's designed to get the discussion going in the right direction.

WATCH VIDEO ONE - DOUG FIELDS (7 MINUTES)

Each week Doug will creatively present 2 of the 10 principles on video. The videos are both engaging and informative. In fact, with a fast moving, seven minute presentation, it will be over before you know it. While short, the videos are created in a way to stimulate thinking so the content will stick.

DISCUSSION QUESTIONS (30 - 45 MINUTES)

After you watch the videos, you'll want enough time for everyone to be able to share (if they desire). If the group is larger than eight people, you might consider dividing the group into two different rooms. One important tip: To keep the environment positive (as you know, parenting can be a sensitive topic), we recommend you encourage people to "speak for themselves instead of speaking for their spouse." Encourage them to share their thoughts and feelings, but to refrain from sharing others' shortcomings.

▶ WATCH VIDEO TWO DOUG & CATHY FIELDS (8 MINUTES) - OPTIONAL

This conversation between Doug & Cathy Fields offers an application of what Doug presented in the previous video. Be sure to preview the video in advance to determine, based on your group, if the conversations with Doug & Cathy would be helpful for group discussion. Some groups like to watch these videos back-to-back and then go into the discussion. You can determine what's best for your group.

⚙ DO (15 MINUTES)

The "Do" Section is to help group members immediately apply one key idea toward their parenting journey for the upcoming week. During this time, you will want to reinforce that they should complete TWO chapters in the Intentional Parenting Workbook between each meetings (reminder: there are 10 chapters in the Workbook and 5 videos—each video covering 2 chapters). Don't let them off the hook! Encourage them to do the work part of the Workbook—this is where the real "gems" and "aha" moments will be discovered. Essentially, this is the "intentional" part of this series. Encourage them to do the reflection, fill out the Workbook, and create their own plan. You might want to close your time in prayer (note: depending on the spiritual depth of your group members you might want to break into smaller groups, so everyone can participate in prayer requests).

HOW TO PREPARE FOR YOUR GROUP

📄 1. PREPARE

As the leader of this group, you don't have to be the expert of parenting. Doug's the expert, so let his video teaching lead the way. If you find your group doesn't have time to answer all the questions in the entire discussion guide… don't stress over it. By preparing ahead of time, you can prioritize the questions for the time you have available. As you get to know the group, choose the questions that you know will lead to good discussion. If your group has been together for a while, you might want to skip the first START question and go for the second question--which is more of an accountability question connected to what they committed to do in the previous meeting.

🤚 2. PRAY FOR YOUR GROUP

If you feel anxious about leading the group or even inadequate, that is perfectly normal, especially if you are leading for the first time. The Bible says, "Do not be anxious about anything, but in every situation, by prayer and petition, with thanksgiving, present your requests to God. And the peace of God, which transcends all understanding, will guard your hearts and your minds in Christ Jesus" (Philippians 4:6-7, NIV). Remember you don't need to be a perfect parent to lead this group.

The video and discussion guide are pretty easy to use, but that doesn't mean you should go into the meeting "cold" spiritually. Commit the meeting to God and then watch Him work.

3. GUIDING THE DISCUSSION - NOT A TEACHER, MORE OF A REFEREE

While everyone should have a chance to share their thoughts and experiences, your job as the leader is to facilitate a discussion, not to teach a class. Your job isn't to do all the talking. You want to make sure everyone gets an opportunity to share. You also want to make sure no one dominates the discussion. If someone tends to jump in on every question, politely say, "Now, on this next question let's hear from a few of you who haven't had a chance to share." If the person dominating the meeting continues to do this, then you might need to talk to them outside of the group meeting.

Tip: don't count on all of the group members working through the chapters in preparation for your meeting. While you hope they will and know they will get the most out of it if they do, prepare your heart for some who don't. Because they are arriving to your meeting with two chapters worth of material, it may take them a few seconds to put their thoughts together and remember where they read that content. Don't feel the pressure to fill the silence. It's okay if the group sits in silence while some thing or look for their answers. Silence may feel painful, but it can also become a catalyst for deep reflection.

4. PRAYING AS A GROUP TOGETHER

Habits are hard to break and often difficult to start. Changing a parent's views and behaviors toward their children requires more than just will power. It requires God's power. Make sure prayer is part of every gathering. You can decide how to best facilitate that prayer time-in smaller groups or all together.

Also, limit the prayer requests to what is personally affecting the group member. Now, they may be concerned about Aunt Gertrude's big toe or something they read about on the internet, but this really isn't the place for these types of prayer requests. As much as you can, keep the focus of the prayer time on the changes the group members need to make related to their parenting style.

ASK FOR VOLUNTEERS

Don't lead the group alone. Just because you are the designated leader, you do not need to do everything for the group. In fact, delegate as much as you possibly can: the refreshments, the home you meet in, and even leading the discussion. If you do this right, you might only need to lead for the first session, then others will lead for the rest. As group members become more involved in the leadership, they will feel a stronger sense of ownership in the group. Pretty soon the group will go from being "your group" to being "our group."

You can do this! Thanks for helping others become Intentional Parents. Trust that God will use your failures and victories to help others. We believe in you and your ability to lead others! — *Doug & Cathy Fields*

SESSION 1: **STRONG BELIEF AND 24/7 ROLE MODEL**

START (15 MINUTES)

If your group is meeting for the first time or if new people have joined your group, take a few minutes to introduce yourselves.

Q: In a word, what do you hope your children will become? And why?

WATCH VIDEO ONE - DOUG FIELDS (7 MINUTES)

For your reference, key phrases from this session are:

- Quick Fix Parenting can lead to disasters
- Parents are the single greatest influence in the life of a child.
- You are under surveillance 24/7
- Good behavior starts with you!
- Admit it when you're wrong
- "Children are a gift from the Lord; they are a reward from him." Psalm 127:3
- Parents need an intentional plan
- Believe in your power to influence

DISCUSSION QUESTIONS (30 MINUTES)

As the group leader, start the conversation. Tell a story about how you had a "Quick Fix" Parenting moment. Try to make it lighthearted. Then guide your groups through these questions:

Q: Everybody falls into Quick Fix Parenting now and again. When is this most likely to happen for you?

Q: When do you most often doubt you have any influence in your children's lives at all?

Q: What makes you nervous about your kids following your example?

Q: What do you want your kids to pick up from you?

Q: Psalms 127:3 says, "Children are a gift from the Lord; they are a reward from him." How do you think God feels about your child?

Q: Have you ever considered having an intentional plan as a parent? How might doing this feel overwhelming?

On this last question, simply point out that the purpose of this series is to help all of us. When the five meeting times are completed we should have a realistic plan that's not overwhelming.

WATCH VIDEO TWO - DOUG & CATHY FIELDS (8 MINUTES) - OPTIONAL

 DO (15 MINUTES)

Q: Based on our discussion today, what is one action you can immediately implement this week?

- Instruct your members to go through the Action 1: Strong Belief and Action 2: 24/7 Role Model in their Workbook. Encourage them to complete the discussion questions and exercises.

- As the meeting comes to a close ask the group for one thing they need prayer for as a parent. This could even be the one thing they want to begin doing this week. Then, pray together.

- Encourage the group to think about other parents who could benefit from this series and invite them to join the group next week.

 END OF SESSION 1 GROUP DISCUSSION

SESSION 2: ENCOURAGING WORDS AND GENUINE AFFECTION

 START (15 MINUTES)

Q: Is it easier for you to be encouraging or critical? Why?

For this next section, break into groups of 3-4 people. Give each person 3 minutes for the following: In the last session, you were challenged to try on one new practice based on the principles of either Strong Belief or 24/7 Role Model. What did you try? How did it go?

 WATCH VIDEO ONE - DOUG FIELDS (8 MINUTES)

For your reference, key phrases from this session are:

- Overwhelm your kids with encouragement
- See and say it positive
- Don't expect encouragement back
- Say it beyond their performance
- Show encourage through affection
- "Love each other with genuine affection, and take delight in honoring each other." Romans 12:10

● DISCUSSION QUESTIONS (30 MINUTES)

As the group leader, start the conversation. Be the first to answer the first question below and then encourage your group to answer the questions.

Q: What did affection and approval look like in the home you grew up in?

Q: In the video, Doug challenged us to "Catch your kids doing things right." How can you discipline yourself to begin seeing your kids with a new, positive, encouraging perspective? What might be difficult about that?

Q: How might you encourage your kids "beyond their performance"?

Q: Is showing physical affection easy or difficult for you? Why? What are some practical ways you might start to become more intentional with your affection?

Q: Romans 12:10 says, "Love each other with genuine affection, and take delight in honoring each other." What are some practical ways you can honor your kids?

▶ WATCH VIDEO TWO - DOUG & CATHY FIELDS (8 MINUTES) - OPTIONAL

⚙ DO (15 MINUTES)

Q: What is one way you can try to reduce the criticism and increase the encouragement with your kids this week?

• Remind your group to go through the Action 3: Encouraging Words, and Action 4: Genuine Affection in your workbook. Work through the discussion questions and exercises.

• As the meeting comes to a close share one thing you need prayer for as a parent. Then, pray together.

✕ END OF SESSION 2 GROUP DISCUSSION

SESSION 3: CONSISTENT PRESENCE AND A PEACEFUL HOME

🚀 START (15 MINUTES)

Q: How often do you look at your phone for updates on social media or texting? Who wants to check it right now because we just brought this up?

Q: What is one situation in which you said "No" to your kids last week where you could have probably said "Yes" to?

▶ WATCH VIDEO ONE - DOUG FIELDS (7 MINUTES)

For your reference, key phrases from this session are:

- Kids need your time.
- Kids would rather have your presence than your presents.
- "This is how much God loved the world. He gave his son, his one and only son." John 3:16a
- Presence requires personal sacrifices.
- Are kids getting your Yes's or your No's?
- Presence might require career sacrifices.
- Kids need your home to be a shelter.
- Presence and a peaceful home go hand-in-hand.

◎ DISCUSSION QUESTIONS (30 MINUTES)

As the group leader, start the conversation. Answer the first question below then encourage your group to answer the questions as well.

1. In the video, Doug said, "Kids would rather have your presence than presents." How do you try to give your presence on a daily or weekly basis to your children? What does "presence" look like in your home?

2. What is something you might have to sacrifice in order to be more present? Why will that sacrifice be difficult for you?

3. John 3:16a says, "This is how much God loved the world. He gave his son, his one and only son." What can we learn from this example of God's love?

4. On a scale of 1 to 10, ten being "heavenly" and one being "Armageddon," how peaceful is your home during a typical week?

5. What is one action you could do to bring more peace into your home immediately?

WATCH VIDEO TWO - DOUG & CATHY FIELDS (8 MINUTES) - OPTIONAL

DO (15 MINUTES)

Q: What is one thing you could say "No" to this week in order to say "Yes" to your kids?

- Ask your group to go through the Action 5: Consistent Presence, and Action 6: A Peaceful Home in your Workbook. Work through the discussion questions and exercises.

- As the meeting comes to a close, share one thing you need prayer for as a parent. This could even be the one thing you want to say "No" to this week in order to say "Yes" to your kids. Then, pray together.

END OF SESSION 3 GROUP DISCUSSION

SESSION 4: DELICATE DISCIPLINE AND ACTIVATE RESPONSIBILITY

START (15 MINUTES)

Q: How were you disciplined as a child?

Q: Do you find yourself doing or saying something that your parents did? How does the discipline you give your children reflect how you were disciplined?

 WATCH VIDEO ONE - DOUG FIELDS (8 MINUTES)

For your reference, key phrases from this session are:

- Discipline is about guidance not punishment.
- Be delicate in discipline.
- Yelling doesn't work.
- When you lose control, they [children] lose respect.
- Your rod and your staff protect and comfort me. Psalm 23:4b
- Every kid needs boundaries.
- 3 Attitudes: Apathy, Blame, Care for Me.
- Stop doing things your kids can do for themselves.
- Teach them that Behaviors have consequences.

⬤ DISCUSSION QUESTIONS (30 MINUTES)

As the group leader, start the conversation. Answer the first question below then encourage your group to answer the questions as well.

Q: In the video, Doug said, "Discipline is about guidance, not punishment. Punishment is a quick fix. Guidance takes time." When your kids push the limits, where do you tend to go in your discipline? How effective is it?

Q: Doug also shared, "When (your kids) see you lose control, they lose respect for you." How many of us felt an "ouch" from that one? When your kids push your buttons, what could be a more effective approach to controlling your response than you normally display?

Q: Currently, when you discipline your kids, does it feel like are you guiding them or punishing them? Why?

Q: Psalm 23:4b says, "Your rod and your staff protect and comfort me." How is your parenting protecting and comforting your child?

Q: In the video, Doug said, "Every kid wants and needs boundaries, and boundaries need to be connected with consequences." What are some examples of boundaries that you've set for your kids? What are examples of consequences when the boundaries are violated? Is it ever difficult for you to carry through with consequences? Why? Why not?

▶ WATCH VIDEO TWO - DOUG & CATHY FIELDS (8 MINUTES) - OPTIONAL

DO (15 MINUTES)

- Q: What is one action from this session that you will put into practice this week?

- For this week, go through the Action 7: Delicate Discipline and Action 8: Activate Responsibility in your Workbook. Work through the discussion questions and exercises.

- As the meeting comes to a close share one thing you need prayer for as a parent. Then, pray together.

✕ END OF SESSION 4 GROUP DISCUSSION

SESSION 5: **POSITIVE MEMORIES AND SERIOUS FUN**

🚀 START (15 MINUTES)

Q: What is one good, strong memory that you have from your childhood that your parent(s) helped create?

Q: Last week you chose one action to take regarding discipline. How did it go?

▶ WATCH VIDEO ONE - DOUG FIELDS (9 MINUTES)

For your reference, key phrases from this session are:

- Are you building good memories or bad memories?
- Create families traditions.
- Traditions create good memories.
- Capture your family memories.
- Prioritize vacations.
- Kids need adventures.
- Create opportunities for fun.
- Take time to make fun happen.
- Ask God for help.
- Come to me all who are weary and I will give you rest. Matthew 11:28
- What will your kids remember about you?

⬤ DISCUSSION QUESTIONS (30 MINUTES)

As the group leader, start the conversation. Answer the first question below then encourage your group to answer the questions as well.

Q: Tell the group about your last family vacation. What do you think your kids remember from the trip? Ask others about their vacations.

Q: What is keeping your family from having more fun?

Q: Doug talked about establishing your own family traditions. What traditions are unique to your family? What are some opportunities for traditions that could you start that might be outside the normal holiday traditions? (i.e. last day of school, last day of summer, etc...)

Q: Matthew 11:28 says, "Come to me all who are weary and I will give you rest." "Parenting" and "Tired" are often synonymous terms... what might seeking rest from God look like?

WATCH VIDEO TWO – DOUG & CATHY FIELDS (8 MINUTES) – OPTIONAL

 DO (15 MINUTES)

- Q: In the video, Doug said, "You can't make more time. You just have to take more time." How can you take more time for your family this week?

- For this week, go through the Action 9: Positive Memories and Action 10: Serious Fun in your Workbook. Work through the discussion questions and exercises.

- As the meeting comes to a close, share one thing you need prayer for as a parent. Then, pray together.

- Can you identify some other parents who you might invite to this type of small group experience? Do you think there are one or two couples from this group who might lead (and co-lead) a new group of parents?

END OF SESSION 5 GROUP DISCUSSION

DOWNLOAD
THE PARENT CUE APP

The Parent Cue App is designed to help every parent do something each week to help move their child toward a deeper faith and a better future.

THEPARENTCUE.ORG/APP